Universal Method

for
Saxophone

by

Paul DeVille

CARL FISCHER®
62 Cooper Square, New York, NY 10003

Copyright © 1908 by Carl Fischer, Inc.
International Copyright Secured.
All rights reserved including performing rights.

O532

ISBN0-8258-0146-X

Author's Note

The author takes great pleasure in stating to the student, that everything which patient research, practical experience and knowledge (of my favorite instrument) could suggest, has been brought to bear to make this the greatest and most comprehensive method for the saxophone ever attempted.

The plan of study is thorough and progressive, and if strictly adhered to, cannot fail to produce a first-class performer.

PAUL DE VILLE

N630

Index

The Saxophone

The Saxophone was invented about the year 1845 by Adolphe Sax, a Belgian, living in Paris, France, who named it after himself.

Originally the Saxophone was very cumbersome and not easy to manipulate, but it has been improved to such an extent within recent years that the most difficult passages may now be executed with comparative ease and little practice. It is now recognized as an indispensible instrument in both brass and reed bands, and has also found a place in the orchestra.

The Saxophone family consists of the Soprano in Bb,—the Alto in Eb,—the Melody Tenor in C,—the Tenor in Bb,—the Baritone in Eb, and the Bass in Bb,—all of which are used with brilliant effect.

The Alto Saxophone is the principal instrument. If two are used they should be Alto and Tenor,—then adding Baritone.

The tonal quality of the Saxophone is very smooth and pleasing to the ear, and its mechanism permits of very brilliant execution.

Position of the Body

The head and body must be kept erect, the weight of the body resting on the right leg, while the left foot should be a little advanced. In sitting, the position in which the instrument is held is just the same.

Manner of Holding the Saxophone

A strap which is attached to the instrument and placed around the neck of the player, enables him to hold it with comfort and steadiness. Such a strap is used on all the models except the Soprano (Clarinet Model).

The right hand is placed at the lower end of the instrument, and the thumb under the hook, which aids in balancing it.

The left hand is placed at the upper part, the thumb on the button below the octave key.

The instrument hangs toward the right just about where the thumb of the right hand touches the vest pocket (Alto Saxophone). The other Saxophones must be held in the same position although the greater size of the instruments might change the position of both arms slightly.

Adjusting the Reed

The reed must be placed on the flat of the mouthpiece so that the tapered edge comes about even with the top end of the mouthpiece. It must be fastened securely at the lower end with the ligature.

Position of the Mouthpiece

The mouthpiece, with the reed underneath, is held between the lips and a little less than half of its curved part is covered.

Draw the lower lip easily over the teeth so that the reed does not touch the teeth. The upper teeth are applied to the mouthpiece.

To Produce the Tone

Keep the lips around the mouthpiece so that it is impossible for any air to escape through the corners of the mouth. Then bring the point of the tongue to the end of the reed, where it is easiest to press it against the mouthpiece. Draw the tongue back sharply allowing the breath to escape into the mouthpiece with a "T" effect.

These movements of the tongue constitute what is called "Tonguing."

The tonguing must be executed vigorously so as to set the column of air into immediate vibration.

Tuning

Before starting to play, always warm up the instrument by blowing your warm breath through it, or by preluding a little if possible. Heat and cold have opposite effects on the Saxophone. When cold, the instrument is flat and when warm it becomes sharp.

The pitch can be regulated to a certain degree by pulling out the mouthpiece when too sharp, and pushing it in further when too flat.

Too much pressure on the reed will make the pitch too sharp, while using too little pressure will create the opposite effect, and the quality of tone will be harsh and disagreeable.

Many good instruments are played out of tune in this way. If the ear is carefully trained, the performer will have little difficulty in playing well in tune.

Care should be taken to avoid swelling of the cheeks as this not only looks bad but impairs the quality of tone and surety of attack. It would be advisable to stand before a mirror occasionally when practicing in order to correct any faulty position, and so that any contortions of the face may be avoided.

Care of the Instrument

Be careful to keep your instrument clean. A small soft brush is very useful for removing dust from between the keys.

If the pads should get wet, they should be dried immediately with a cloth.

Dust or dampness harden the pads and clog the openings, preventing proper covering of the holes.

When the pads become hard and stiff they should be replaced with new ones.

The springs should be oiled occasionally.

Before Playing

Be **sure** that your reed is not too stiff or too soft. If too stiff, it not only produces a dry and harsh tone, but is also injurious to the player. If too soft, the tone will be thick and unnatural. This defect is particularly noticeable in the lower and higher registers. The lower notes will not respond readily except with exertion, indicating that your reed is too hard, and when the higher notes sound thin and unnatural and are unresponsive, it is generally because the reed is too soft. A reed which answers both purposes must be used.

Before applying the reed to the mouthpiece, it should be moistened or wet at the thinner end. See that it is not curved as that would stop the tone production.

To straighten a reed, moisten it, then place the curved part on a flat surface pressing it there with your thumb for a few seconds.

After Playing

Remove the reed and dry it. Then dry and clean the saliva from the mouthpiece. Any moisture on the keys or pads should also be removed with a soft cloth.

It is advisable to keep the reed removed from the mouthpiece until it is to be used again.

The reed should be placed in a box, preferably against a piece of glass. In this manner it will keep straight.

How to Practice

Practice regularly each day, if possible.

Do not attempt too much at first and do not get discouraged if the first studies prove tiresome and monotonous.

Play all music exactly as written.

Do not over-exert yourself when playing.

Practice in such a manner that you can play without apparent effort, and can derive pleasure from it.

Do not practice too long at one time. Too much or too strenuous practice is as harmful as too little.

Listen carefully and you will hear if a tone is good or bad.

Hold your instrument steady so that it cannot move and interfere with the good quality of tone and the execution.

What to Practice

Practice whatever may be necessary and what you are not familiar with. Sustained tones should be practiced a few minutes each day before anything else. This helps to strengthen the lips and will improve the quality of tone. This is very important, as a good tone is the performer's most valuable asset.

Do not fail to practice all sorts of exercises and scales.

In striking tones, especially in rapid execution, the fingers and the tongue must work simultaneously.

Give particular attention to the quality of tone, also to style of performance and to phrasing.

Avoid the "tremolo" or "vibrato" style of playing. See that your tone is absolutely clear and pure.

Transposition

Learn to transpose. This is a positive necessity for professionals and is very convenient and desirable for amateurs. It should not be studied however, until the pupil has a fair knowledge of the rudiments of music and is beyond the first stages of playing.

It is very essential that the performer who expects to play in orchestra, should have knowledge of the Bass Clef, the Tenor Clef and the Treble Clef, which are the three principal ones.

With a knowledge of the Treble and Bass, all the other Clefs are easily acquired, and transposition becomes very simple and easy.

A . . . . to, in or at; *a tempo*, in time
Accelerando (accel.). Gradually increasing the speed
Accent . . . . . . Emphasis on certain parts of the measure
Adagio . . . . Slowly leisurely
Ad libitum (ad lib.) . At pleasure; not in strict time
A due (a 2). . . . . To be played by both instruments
Agitato . . . . . . Restless, with agitation
Al or Alla. . . . . In the style of
Alla Marcia . . . . In the style of a March
Allegretto. . . . . Diminutive of allegro; moderately fast, lively; faster than *andante*; slower than *allegro*
Allegro . . . . . . Lively; brisk, rapid.
Allegro assai. . . . Very rapidly
Amoroso . . . . . . Affectionately
Andante . . . . . . In moderately slow time
Andantino . . . . . Diminutive of *andante*; strictly *slower* than andante, but often used in the reverse sense
Anima, con } . . . With animation
Animato
A piacere. . . . . . At pleasure; equivalent to *ad libitum*
Appassionato. . . . Impassioned
Arpeggio . . . . . . A broken chord
Assai . . . . Very; *Allegro assai*, very rapidly
A tempo . . . . . . In the original tempo
Attacca . . . . . . Attack or begin what follows without pausing
Barcarolle . . . . . A Venetian boatman's song
Bis . . . . Twice, repeat the passage
Bravura . . . . . . Brilliant; bold; spirited
Brillante. . . . . . Showy, sparkling, brilliant
Brio, con . . . . . With much spirit
Cadenza . . . . . . An elaborate, florid passage introduced as an embellishment
Cantabile. . . . . . In a singing style
Canzonetta. . . . . A short song or air
Capriccio a . . . . At pleasure, ad libitum
Cavatina . . . . . An air, shorter and simpler than the aria, and in one division, without Da Capo
Chord . . . . The harmony of three or more tones of different pitch produced simultaneously
Coda . . . . A supplement at the end of a composition
Col or con . . . . . With
Crescendo (cresc.) . Swelling; increasing in loudness
Da or dal . . . . . From
Da Capo (D. C.) . . From the beginning
Dal Segno (D. S.). . From the sign
Decrescendo (decresc.) Decreasing in strength
Diminuendo (dim.). Gradually softer
Divisi. . . . . . . Divided, each part to be played by a separate instrument
Dolce (dol.) . . . . Softly; sweetly
Dolcissimo . . . . . Very sweetly and softly
Dominant. . . . . . The fifth tone in the major or minor scale
Duet or Duo . . . . A composition for two performers
E. . . . . And
Elegante . . . . . . Elegant, graceful
Energico . . . . . . With energy, vigorously
Enharmonic . . . . Alike in pitch, but different in notation
Espressivo . . . . . With expression
Finale . . . . The concluding movement
Fine . . . . The end
Forte (f) . . . . . Loud
Forte-piano (fp) . . Accent strongly, diminishing instantly to piano
Fortissimo (ff). . . Very loud
Forsando (fz >) . . Indicates that a note or chord is to be strongly accented
Forza . . . . Force of tone
Fuoco, con . . . . . With fire; with spirit
Giocoso . . . . . . Joyously; playfully
Giusto. . . . . . . Exact; in strict time
Grandioso. . . . . Grand; pompous; majestic
Grave . . . . Very slow and solemn
Grazioso . . . . . Gracefully
Harmony. . . . . . In general, a combination of tones, or chords, producing music
Key note . . . . . The first degree of the scale, the tonic
Largamente . . . . Very broad in style
Larghetto. . . . . . Slow, but not so slow as Largo; nearly like Andantino
Largo. . . . . . . Broad and slow; the slowest tempo-mark
Legato. . . . . . . Smoothly, the reverse of staccato
Ledger-line. . . . . A small added line above or below the staff
Lento . . . . Slow, between Andante and Largo
L'istesso tempo. . . In the same time, (or tempo)
Loco. . . . . In place. Play as written, no longer an octave higher or lower
Ma . . . . But
Ma non troppo. . . Lively, but not too much so
Maestoso . . . . . Majestically; dignified
Maggiore . . . . . Major Key
Marcato. . . . . . Marked
Meno . . . . Less
Meno mosso . . . . Less quickly
Mezzo . . . . Half; moderately

Mezzo-piano (mp) . Moderately soft
Minore . . . . . . Minor Key
Moderato. . . . . . Moderately. *Allegro moderato*, moderately fast
Molto. . . . . . . Much; very
Morendo . . . . . . Dying away
Mosso. . . . . . . Equivalent to rapid. *Piu mosso*, quicker.
Moto. . . . . Motion. *Con moto*, with animation
Non. . . . . Not
Notation . . . . . . The art of representing musical sounds by means of written characters
Obbligata . . . . . An indispensable part
Opus (Op.). . . . . A work.
Ossia . . . . Or; or else. Generally indicating an easier method
Ottava (8va) . . . To be played an octave higher
Pause (⌒). . . . . The sign indicating a pause or rest.
Perdendosi . . . . . Dying away gradually
Piacere, a . . . . . At pleasure
Pianissimo (pp) . . Very softly
Piano (p) . . . . . Softly
Piu. . . . . More
Piu Allegro . . . . More quickly
Piu tosto. . . . . . Quicker
Poco or un poco . . A little
Poco a poco . . . . Gradually, by degrees; little by little
Poco piu mosso . . A little faster
Poco meno . . . . . A little slower
Poco piu. . . . . . A little faster
Poi . . . . Then; afterwards
Pomposo. . . . . . Pompous; grand
Prestissimo . . . . As quickly as possible
Presto . . . . Very quick; faster than *Allegro*
Primo (Imo). . . . The first
Quartet . . . . . . A piece of music for four performers.
Quasi. . . . . . . As if; in the style of
Quintet. . . . . . . A piece of music for five performers
Rallentando (rall.) Gradually slower
Replica. . . . . . . Repetition. *Senza replica*, without repeats
Rinforsando . . . . With special emphasis
Ritardando (rit.) . Gradually slower and slower
Risoluto . . . . . Resolutely; bold; energetic
Ritenuto . . . . . . In slower time
Scherzando. . . . . Playfully; sportively
Secondo (2do) . . . The second singer, instrumentalist or part
Segue. . . . . . . Follow on in similar style
Semplice . . . . . Simply; unaffectedly
Senza. . . . . . . Without. *Senza sordino* without mute
Sforzando (sf). . . Forcibly; with sudden emphasis
Simile or Simili. . In like manner
Smorzando (smorz) Diminishing in sound. Equivalent to *Morendo*
Solo. . . . . For one performer only. *Soli*; for all
Sordino . . . . . . A mute. *Con sordino*, with the mute
Sostenuto. . . . . . Sustained; prolonged.
Sotto . . . . Below; under. *Sotto voce*, in a subdued tone
Spirito. . . . . . . Spirit. *con Spirito* with spirit
Staccato. . . . . . Detached; separate
Stentando . . . . . Dragging or retarding the tempo
Stretto or stretta. An increase of speed. *Piu stretto* faster
Subdominant. . . . The fourth tone in the diatonic scale
Syncopation. . . . Change of accent from a strong beat to a weak one.
Tacet. . . . . . . "Is silent" Signified that an instrument or vocal part, so marked, is omitted during the movement or number in question
Tempo. . . . . . . Movement; rate of speed.
Tempo primo . . . Return to the original tempo.
Tenuto (ten.) . . . Held for the full value.
Thema or Theme . The subject or melody.
Tonic. . . . . . . The key-note of any scale.
Tranquillo . . . . . Quietly.
Tremolando, Tremolo A tremulous fluctuation of tone.
Trio. . . . . A piece of music for three performers.
Triplet . . . . . . A group of three notes to be performed in the time of two of equal value in the regular rhythm.
Troppo . . . . . . Too; too much. *Allegro, ma non troppo*, not too quickly.
Tutti . . . . All; all the instruments.
Un. . . . . A, one, an.
Una corda . . . . . On one string.
Variatione . . . . . The transformation of a melody by means of harmonic, rhythmic and melodic changes and embellishments.
Veloce. . . . . . . Quick, rapid, swift.
Vibrato . . . . . . A wavering tone-effect, which should be sparingly used.
Vivace . . . . . . With vivacity; bright; spirited.
Vivo. . . . . Lively; spirited
Volti Subito V. S. . Turn over quickly.

HOW TO MAKE YOUR OWN REEDS

While reeds of the best quality may now be obtained in music supply houses, some performers prefer to make their own reeds, and at least some knowledge of the process of reed-making or correcting faults is invaluable. (The figures interspersed refer to diagrams on following page.)

First cut off a piece of cane the thickness of a half dollar coin (1) and of the size of the *lay* (3) (The part of the mouthpiece where the reed is laid and held by the ligature or reed-holder).Then rub the inside part of the cane on a broad fine cut file until the surface is perfectly flat, after which it may be placed on the *lay* (3) and the screws of reed-holder tightened to ascertain if the opening (5) is correct. Holding the mouthpiece sideways against the light the opening (5) should extend downward about one inch.   Remove the reed from mouthpiece and with a sharp knife trim down gradually from centre (6) to top (7) being careful not to take too much off at first as later adjustment must be allowed for. The edges should be rounded from where the cutting begins (8) and show an elongated angle from the middle. The cane should be thicker in the middle (9) than at the edges (10). The thin end of reed can be shaped with a sharp pair of scissors or a reed-cutter. If, on trial, the reed proves too hard, file off the thickness at top of reed, sloping toward edges (11). If the top is already thin enough, file off between the centre (6) and the top (7), but with great care, for should too much be taken off, the tone will be spoiled. Then with a very smooth file file straight across the top of reed to a depth of $\frac{1}{8}$ of an inch downward; this will leave thin part even and almost transparent. Again place the reed on *lay* (3) and give a side glance at the opening (5); should it be too close, loosen the top screw of reed-holder and tighten the bottom screw. Reverse the process if the opening is too large. The flat surface of the reed (2) may become warped and uneven, in which case rub carefully on the large file or on the finest sandpaper laid on a perfectly smooth or flat surface, preferably, plate glass.

When left on the mouth-piece for a few days, all the small faults in a reed may vanish; but the real fault may be in the mouth-piece, if located there take the mouth-piece to the maker or a repair shop for refacing.

If the reed still remains too hard, adjust it on *lay* so as to show a trifle below top of the mouth-piece, (13) if too soft adjust it to show above the top (14), this experiment will at once show the defect. In the first case reduce the reed at end of the curve (15), in the second case, cut off the top (16)

Future warping of the reed may be corrected by using large file or sandpaper, but carefully avoid making reed too thin at the heel (17).

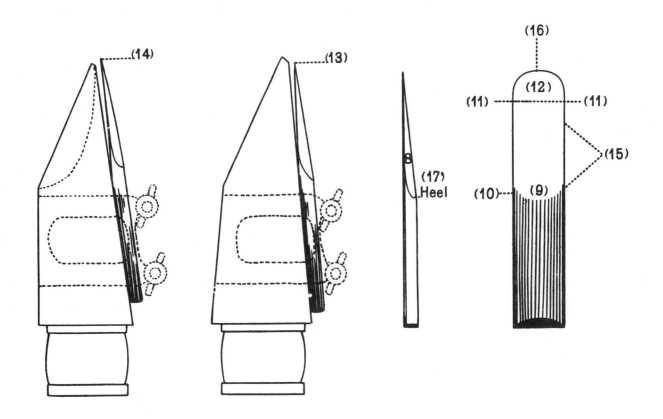

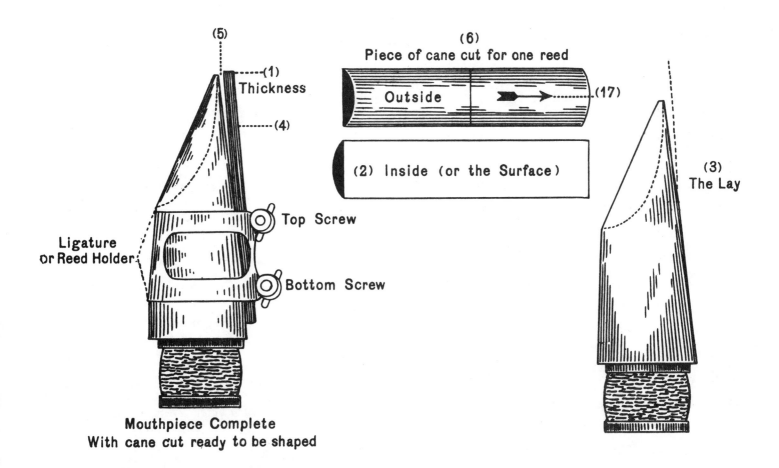

(14)
(13)
(16)
(12)
(11)   (11)
(15)
(10)   (9)
8
(17)
Heel

(5)
(1)
(1) Thickness
(4)

(6)
Piece of cane cut for one reed

Outside   (17)

(2) Inside (or the Surface)

(3)
The Lay

Top Screw

Ligature
or Reed Holder

Bottom Screw

Mouthpiece Complete
With cane cut ready to be shaped

RUDIMENTS OF MUSIC

Before the student can commence to play any instrument it is necessary that he should be acquainted with the rudiments of musical *Notation*.

The signs, which indicate pitch and duration of a musical sound, are called *Notes* figured thus: o 𝅝 𝅗𝅥 ♪ ♪ 𝅘𝅥𝅮 etc.

They are named after seven letters of the alphabet; C. D. E. F. G. A. B. and are written on, between, above or below five parallel lines, ≣ called the Stave, the names of which are determined by *Clefs*, placed on different lines.

For this instrument, only the treble or G 'clef 𝄞 is used, which is placed on the second line.

The names of the notes on the five lines are:
E G B D F

of the four spaces between the lines: 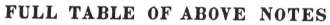 of the two above and below the lines
F A C E
D G

These eleven notes are insufficient to indicate the full compass of Sounds in use.

Ledger lines have therefore to be added, above and below the stave in order to signify higher and deeper sounds.

Notes of the ledger lines above the stave
A B C D E F G A

Notes of the ledger lines below the stave
C B A G

FULL TABLE OF ABOVE NOTES

G A B C D E F G A B C D E F G A B C D E F G A B C

DURATION OF NOTES

Notes may be of longer or shorter *Duration* which is shown by the peculiar form of each note.

Forms of different notes

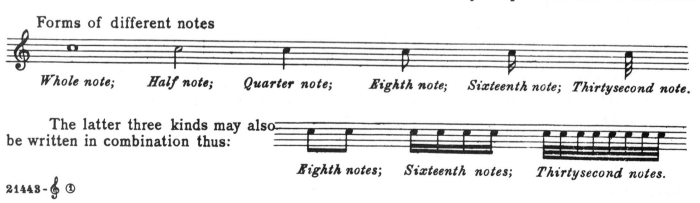
Whole note;   *Half note;*   *Quarter note;*   *Eighth note;*   *Sixteenth note;*   *Thirtysecond note.*

The latter three kinds may also be written in combination thus:
Eighth notes;   *Sixteenth notes;*   *Thirtysecond notes.*

COMPARATIVE TABLE OF THE RELATIVE VALUE OF NOTES

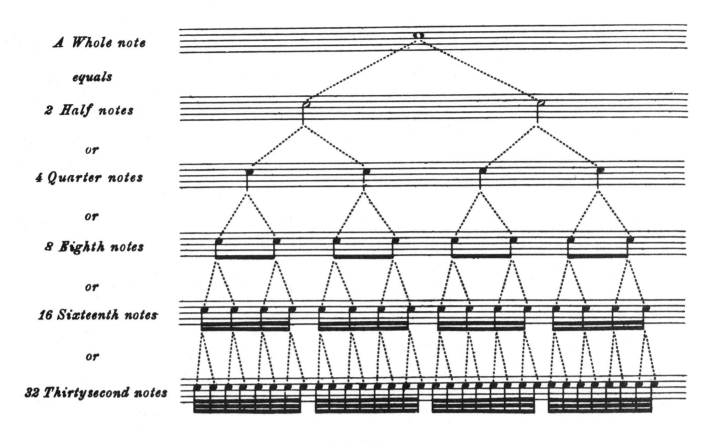

A Whole note

equals

2 Half notes

or

4 Quarter notes

or

8 Eighth notes

or

16 Sixteenth notes

or

32 Thirtysecond notes

BARS

Notes are systematically arranged into *bars,* marked by one or two lines drawn across the stave.

One line ☰ is placed after each bar and each bar contains the same number or value of notes, and each bar must last precisely the same length of time. The end of a part of a composition is marked with two lines or a double bar, and if either two or four dots are found by the side of the double bar thus: ☰ the whole part from the pre-ceding double bar, or if there is no earlier double bar then from the beginning of the piece, is to be played again. This is called a *Repeat.*

RESTS

Instead of a note a *Rest* of equal value can be placed.

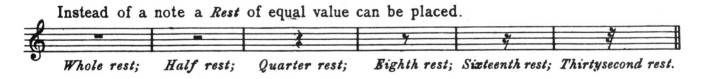

Whole rest;   Half rest;   Quarter rest;   Eighth rest;   Sixteenth rest;   Thirtysecond rest.

DOTS

A *Dot* placed after any note or rest increases its value one half, thus:

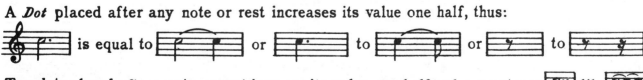

is equal to ☰ or ☰ to ☰ or ☰ to ☰

Two dots placed after a note or rest increase its value one half and a quarter or ☰ like ☰ etc.

21443-𝄞 ②

TRIPLETS, SEXTUPLETS, AND ODD GROUPS

Triplets are marked by a *3* being put over a group of three notes.   Sextuplets are marked by a *6* being placed over a group of six notes.   Three quarter notes marked thus must be played in the same time as two quarter notes not so marked; or six eighth notes in the time of four eighth notes not so marked.   There are also groups of five seven and nine notes etc.

TIME SIGNATURES

In order to know how many quarter notes, eighth notes or sixteenth notes a bar contains, special figures are placed at the beginning of a movement.

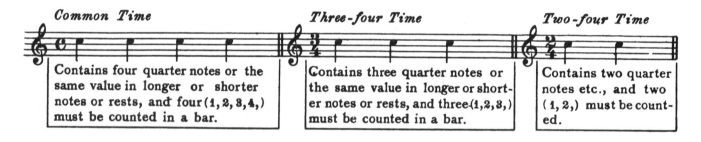

Common Time

Contains four quarter notes or the same value in longer or shorter notes or rests, and four (1, 2, 3, 4,) must be counted in a bar.

Three-four Time

Contains three quarter notes or the same value in longer or shorter notes or rests, and three (1, 2, 3,) must be counted in a bar.

Two-four Time

Contains two quarter notes etc., and two (1, 2,) must be counted.

TABLE OF TIME SIGNATURES

When a line is drawn through the **C** thus: **¢**, which is called alla breve, two is counted in a bar.

SCALES

The ladder-like succession of eight sounds, starting from any note and ascending or descending by tones and semitones in regular order, is called a *Scale,* and each note of a scale is called a *Degree.*

Between these eight degrees there are seven intervals or distances, five of which are tones, and two semitones.

There are two principal kinds of scales, termed *Major* and *Minor,* whose ascension or descension is diatonical: i.e. in tones and semitones, and a third kind, whose ascension and descension is chromatic: i.e. only in semitones.

For the present, only the *Major* scale will be discussed. In the *Major* scale the semitones are situated between the third and fourth and the seventh and eighth degrees of the scale.

EXAMPLE

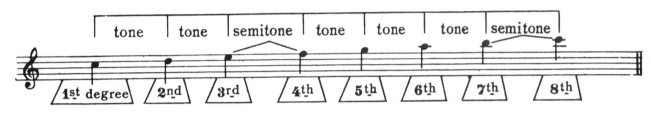

Each diatonic scale derives its name from the name of the note on the first degree or the *root.*

There are twelve major and twelve minor scales; but not to burden the student with their combination at present, only the scale of C will be given.

The distance from one note to another is called an *Interval.* Two notes placed on the same degree do not produce any interval, they are said to be in *Unison.*

The intervals are named: the Second, the Third, the Fourth, the Fifth, the Sixth, the Seventh, the Octave, etc.

EXAMPLE

SHARPS

A scale may be formed on any note, but in order to produce semitones between the third and fourth and seventh and eighth degrees in any order but the scale of C major, it is required to employ certain characters, which raise degrees, or restore the pitch of any note in the scale.

One of these characters is called a sharp (♯), which, when prefixed to a note raises it a half tone.

The number of sharps employed in a scale depends upon which note the scale is founded.

The sharps succeed each other in the following order:

F sharp,   C sharp,   G sharp,   D sharp,   A sharp,   E sharp,   B sharp.

Thus it will be seen that if one sharp is employed it must be prefixed to F, consequently all F's in that piece must be raised half a tone. When two sharps are employed all F's and C's must be raised, and when three sharps are employed all F's, C's and G's must be raised and so on.

TABLE OF SIGNATURES OF SHARP KEYS

Number of Sharps:	1	2	3	4	5	6	7
Names of the Keys:	G	D	A	E	B	F♯	C♯

FLATS

A flat (♭) prefixed to a note lowers it half a tone. The flats succeed each other in the following order:

B flat,   E flat,   A flat,   D flat,   G flat,   C flat,   F flat.

The same rule concerning signatures as with sharps is to be observed here.

TABLE OF SIGNATURES OF FLAT KEYS

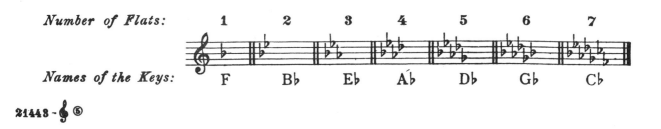

Number of Flats:	1	2	3	4	5	6	7
Names of the Keys:	F	B♭	E♭	A♭	D♭	G♭	C♭

THE MINOR SCALES

Every major scale has its relative minor, the root of which is to be found on the sixth degree of the major scale. Both scales bear the same signature. There are two kinds of *minor* scales, the *harmonic* and the *melodic* form.

THE MELODIC MINOR SCALE

The ascending of the melodic *minor* scale differs from the descending, the former having its sixth and seventh degree raised by *accidentals not essential to the key*. In the ascending, semitones are situated between the second and third and the seventh and eighth degrees, and in the descending between the sixth and fifth and the third and second degrees.

SCALE OF A MINOR
Without Signature; Relative to C major.

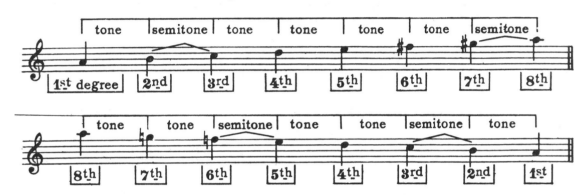

TABLE OF MINOR KEYS WITH THEIR RELATION TO MAJOR

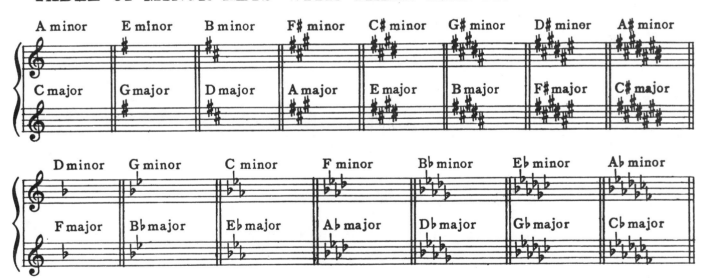

THE HARMONIC MINOR SCALE

The Harmonic Minor Scale differs from the Melodic, as only its 7th degree is raised by an accidental, which remains, whether ascending or descending.

SCALE OF A MINOR

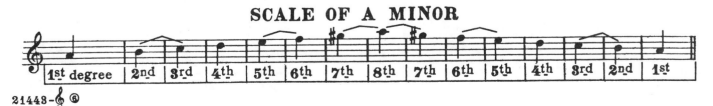

THE NATURAL ♮

In order to restore a note which has been raised by a sharp(♯)or lowered by a flat(♭), a *Natural*(♮) is employed which restores it to its original pitch.

Thus 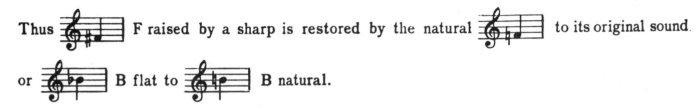 F raised by a sharp is restored by the natural to its original sound.

or B flat to B natural.

THE DOUBLE SHARP ×

By prefixing a double sharp × to a note the same must be raised a whole tone.

Thus F double sharp 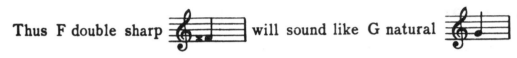 will sound like G natural

THE DOUBLE FLAT ♭♭

A double flat ♭♭ prefixed to a note depresses the note a whole tone. Thus B♭♭

(double flat) will sound like A natural

THE PAUSE ⌢

A Pause ⌢ placed over a note, means that the note can be sustained to an indefinite length at the performer's pleasure; the counting being interrupted.

THE CHROMATIC SCALE

Consists of a succession of semitones, which, in ascending are designated by sharps, and in descending by flats.

ABBREVIATIONS

Abbreviations are employed in written music to avoid repetitions of a single note or passage.

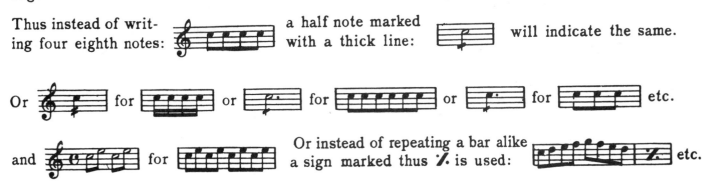

Thus instead of writing four eighth notes: ... a half note marked with a thick line: ... will indicate the same.

Or ... for ... or ... for ... or ... for ... etc.

and ... for ... Or instead of repeating a bar alike a sign marked thus ⅞. is used: ... etc.

TRANSPOSITION OF THE KEYS

When C is taken as **1**, the scale or key is said to be in its natural position; but either of the other letters may be taken as **1**, in which case the scale is said to be *transposed*. As **1** is the basis of the scale, the foundation on which it rests, so the letter which is taken for this sound is called the *Key-note*. Thus, if the scale be in its natural position, it is said to be in the key of C; if G be taken as **1**, the scale is in the key of G; if D be taken as **1**, the scale is in the key of D; and so on with the rest of the seven letters; which ever letter is taken as **1**, that letter becomes the key-note of the scale.

In transposing the scale, the order of the intervals or tones and semitones, must be preserved. Thus, the interval must always be a *tone* from **1** to **2**, a *tone* from **2** to **3**, a *semitone* from **3** to **4**, a *tone* from **4** to **5**, a *tone* from **5** to **6**, a *tone* from **6** to **7** and a *semitone* from **7** to **8**. The interval from one letter to another letter is also the same and cannot be changed thus it is always a *tone* from C to D, and from D to E, a *semitone* from E to F, a *tone* from F to G, from G to A, from A to B, and a *semitone* from B to C. In the transposition of the scale therefore it becomes necessary to introduce sharps and flats, or to substitute sharped or flatted letters for the natural letters, so as to preserve the proper order of the intervals.

First transposition by sharps from C to G, a fifth higher, or a fourth lower.

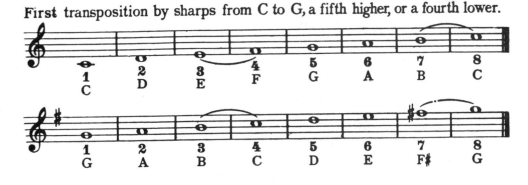

The same method is followed in the transpositions by sharps, viz: the fifth above or the fourth below is taken as **1** of a new key in every succeeding transposition and an additional sharp will be required in every succeeding transposition.

To transpose the scale by flats, we take the fourth (instead of the fifth) of every new scale. F is the fourth of C; hence it is **1** of the new scale (key of F.) The order of intervals must be the same in the flat key as in the sharp; hence the B must be made flat.

It is clear that there must be a tonal difference between the third trom C to E and the third from E to E♭. It has been stated that the tonal difference between two notes on adjacent degrees of the staff is not always the same, likewise intervals of a third, fourth, etc., vary as to tonal content. The third from C to E is called a Major (Large) Third (2 full Tones), that from C to E♭ is called a Minor (Small) Third (1 tone and a Semi-Tone). This classification of intervals belongs properly to the study of Harmony and does not necessarily concern the student now. It will be sufficient to make the transposition by intervals as directed, and remember the scale of the *new key* we are playing in.

DIFFERENT SHADES OF TONE

p   means: *piano*, soft

pp means: *pianissimo*, very soft

f   means: *forte*, loud

ff means: *fortissimo*, very loud

mf means: *mezzoforte*, moderately loud

cresc. or ⊲ means *crescendo*, increasing the sound

dim. decresc. or ⊳ means *diminuendo*, *decrescendo*, diminishing the sound

sf, rf or > means *sforzando*, *rinforzando*, sharply accentuated

fp means: *forte-piano*, loud and immediately soft again

GRACES, EMBELLISHMENTS OR ORNAMENTS OF MELODY

THE APPOGGIATURA

The appoggiatura is a grace note placed above or below a principal note.   When it is placed above, it is always at the interval of either a tone or a semitone.   When it is placed below the principal note it should always be at the interval of a semitone.   When the appoggiatura is written so  the value of it is one half of the following note.

When crossed by a small line, thus:  its value is but one fourth of the note that follows it.

EXAMPLES

Written thus:

Played thus:

There is also a double appoggiatura which is composed of two grace notes placed: the first, one degree below the principal note, and the second, one degree above.

Written thus:

EXAMPLE.

Played thus:

THE GRUPPETTO OR TURN

Is composed of three grace notes placed between or after a principal note. The turn is marked thus. ∾. A small sharp placed under some of the signs thus: ∾ indicates that the lowest of the three grace notes is sharpened. Should the sharp be placed above the sign thus ∾, the upper grace note must be sharpened; or in case of a sharp above and below the sign ∾, the upper and lower grace note must be sharpened. The same rule applies to flats, only that the grace notes must be lowered half a tone in that case.

EXAMPLES

With sharps and flats

THE PASSING SHAKE

The passing shake, often written thus ᴡ, must be played quick and round in the following manner:

THE SHAKE

The shake or trillo, marked thus 𝄐 consists in the alternate repetition of the note marked, with the note in the next degree above it.

EXAMPLE

Chain of Shakes

Improvements added to the
Evette and Schaeffer System of Saxophones.

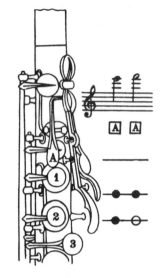

First New Patent Key of High E♮ and F.

The notes E♮ and F above the staff are obtained upon all Saxophones by using simultaneously three or four keys; the hand to catch these keys must quit its natural position; and to return again is very difficult.

With Evette and Schaeffer's new patent key Ⓐ they suppress that difficulty as shown in the following examples.

The key Ⓐ shuts automatically the plate (or plateau) of the first finger.

It is very easy to see the many advantages of this new fingering.

Note: See Exercises for this new fingering on pages **90 & 91.**

Second New Patent E♭ Key.

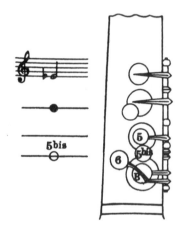

The passing from B♮, C♮ and C♯ to E♭ is very difficult on all Saxophones, and requires great practice and study; various mechanisms have been tried in remedying this inconvenience; Evette and Schaeffer claim they have thoroughly succeeded by obtaining the emission of the E♭ through the hole of the E♮.

The E♭ is obtained by lowering the plate 5bis with the second finger right hand, third finger being raised. The little finger, which usually takes the E♭ key, thus remains free and the passing from B♮, C♮ and C♯ to E♭ becomes quite easy.

Note: See Exercises for this new fingering on page **75.**

Last Improvement on the
Evette and Schaeffer System of Saxophones.

Three New Patent Keys for the Low B♭, B♮ and C♯.

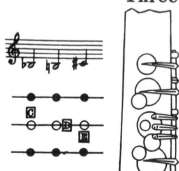

Owing to the successive improvements made by them to the Saxophone, the fingering of that instrument has become very easy.

But it remained yet a question to be solved, viz: how to be able to obtain the low notes with both hands. However, nothing was more easy, but that ought to be met with.

Such question to-day was solved out, since, without any new mechanism, the three notes, low B♭, B♮ and C♯ made by the little finger of the left hand, are also made with the second (or middle) finger of the right hand, by means of three double spatulus.

It is easy to account for the fact that; since these three notes are made indifferently with both hands, thence all the most difficult passages become very easy to be made out.

Note: See Exercises for this new fingering on pages **197, 198, 199 & 200.**

Preparatory Exercises

For the Production of Tone and Forming the Embouchure.

Note: It is taken for granted, that, the Student has already made himself acquainted with the Rudiments of Music.

Observation: Each note, in the following exercises, should be touched softly with the tongue by pronouncing the letter *T;* the breath must be emitted evenly, so as to produce a long and equal note.

Each exercise between repeat-bars should be repeated till the execution is perfect; and be finished with the note surmounted by the pause: (⌒).

Exercises.

Pronounce the letter *T* for each note.   Breath should be taken at the sign: (ꭡ).

28

* Use *no* more pressure for this *C than for the C in the third space of the staff.

15.

*C

Diatonic Scale of C major.

This sign ∨ shows where the half tones occur.

16.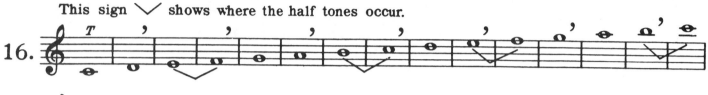

Exercises on Intervals.

Thirds.

Give a lighter pressure on the reed to produce the lower notes.

17.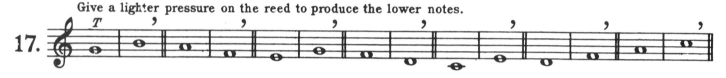

Pass from one note to another without pressure of the lower lip.

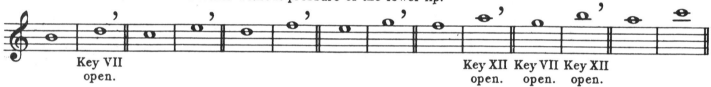

Key VII
open.

Key XII   Key VII   Key XII
open.   open.   open.

Fourths.

18.

Fifths.

19.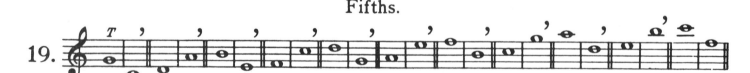

Sixths.

20.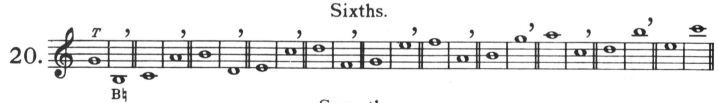

B♮

Sevenths.

21.

Octaves.

Ninths.

Shading.

Diminuendo: (gradual diminuition of sound.)

Crescendo - Diminuendo: (increase and decrease of tone.)

Exercise to Acquire Evenness in Passing from B to C.

Exercises on Time.

The Student will now observe the value of the notes.

Common or Four-four time.

Count mentally: 1, 2, 3, 4. 1, 2, 3, 4. 1, 2, 3, 4. 1, 2, 3, 4. 1, 2, 3, 4. 1, 2, 3, 4. 1, 2, 3, 4. 1, 2, 3, 4.

1 2 3 4.

1, 2, 3, 4. 1, 2, 3, 4.

Count: 1, 2, 3, 4. 1, 2, 3, 4. 1, 2, 3, 4. 1, 2, 3, 4.

Two-four time.

32. Count: *1, 2. 1, 2. 1, 2.*

33. Count: *1, 2. 1, 2.*

Three-four time. Observe the notes with dots placed after them.

34. Count: *1, 2, 3. 1, 2, 3. 1, 2, 3.*   *1, 2, 3.*

35. Count: *1, 2, 3. 1, 2, 3.*   *1, 2, 3.*   *1, 2, 3. 1, 2, 3.*

Six-eight time.

36. Count: *1, 2. 1, 2.*   *1, 2.*   *1, 2.*

Count also: *1,2,3,4,5,6. 1,2,3,4,5,6.*   *1,2,3,4,5,6.*

Exercises in Slurring.

These exercises should be played at first slowly, and when the fingering has been acquired smoothly, they should be repeated many times, gradually increasing in speed.

Tongue only the first note of the Slur, and continue the tone till the second.

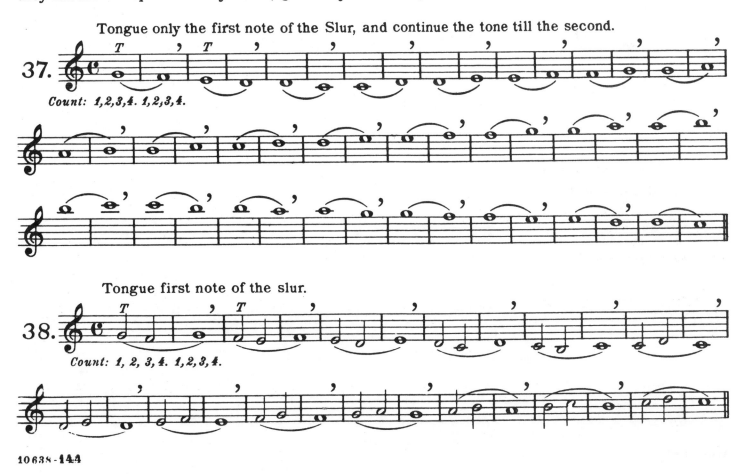

37. Count: *1,2,3,4. 1,2,3,4.*

Tongue first note of the slur.

38. Count: *1, 2, 3, 4. 1,2,3,4.*

39. Count: 1, 2, 3, 4.

40. Count: 1, 2, 3, 4.

41. Count: 1, 2, 3, 4.

Observe the Rests.   Seconds.

42. Count: 1, 2, 3, 4. 1, 2, 3, 4. 1, 2, 3, 4.

43. Count: *1, 2, 3, 4. 1, 2, 3, 4. 1, 2, 3, 4.*

44. Count: *1, 2, 3, 4. 1, 2, 3, 4.*

Thirds.

45. Count: *1, 2, 3, 4. 1, 2, 3, 4.*

34

Fourths.

Fifths.

Sixths.

Sevenths.

Octaves.

Progressive Exercises on Time.

Observe the Rests.

Common or Four-four time.

62. Count: 1, 2, 3, 4. 1, 2, 3, 4.

63. Count: 1, 2, 3, 4.

64. Count: 1, 2, 3, 4. 1, 2, 3, 4. 1, 2, 3, 4. 1, 2, 3, 4.

1, 2, 3, 4.

Syncopation.

65. Count: 1, 2, 3, 4. 1, 2, 3, 4.

Three-four time.

66. Count: 1, 2, 3. 1, 2, 3.

67.
Count: 1, 2, 3.   1, 2, 3.

Three-eight time.

68.
Count: 1, 2, 3.   1, 2, 3.   1, 2, 3.   1, 2, 3.

Six-four time.

69.
Count: 1, 2, 3, 4, 5, 6.   1, 2, 3, 4, 5, 6.   1, 2, 3,   4, 5, 6.

1   2   3   4   5   6

Nine-four time.

70.
Count: 1, 2, 3, 4, 5, 6, 7, 8, 9.   1, 2, 3, 4, 5, 6, 7, 8, 9.

Count: 1,   2,   3.   1,   2,   3.   1,   2,   3.   1,   2,   3.

1,   2,   3.   1,   2,   3.   1,   2,   3.   1, 2, 3.

Nine-eight time.

71.
Count: 1, 2, 3, 4, 5, 6, 7, 8, 9.

Count: 1,   2,   3.   1,   2, 3.

1, 2, 3, 4, 5, 6, 7, 8, 9.

1,   2,   3.

Observe the Articulation.

Twelve-eight time.

Exercises on Dotted Notes.

Exercises on Rests.

The Rest on the first beat.

The Rest on the second beat.

The Rest on the third beat.

82.

Count: 1, 2, 3, 4.   1, 2, 3, 4.

The Rest on the fourth beat.

83.

Count: 1, 2, 3, 4.   1, 2, 3, 4.

The Rest on different beats.

84.

Count: 1, 2, 3, 4.   1, 2, 3, 4.

Eighth Rest on the first and third beats.

85.

Count: 1,   2,   3,   4.

44

10638-247

Twenty Progressive Exercises.
For Saxophone.

The Student should play all the following exercises slowly at first, until he is certain of the fingering. Repeating each over and over again, he should quicken the tempo, so as to acquire facility of rapid execution, and never proceed to a new exercise until the one in hand has been mastered.

PAUL de VILLE.

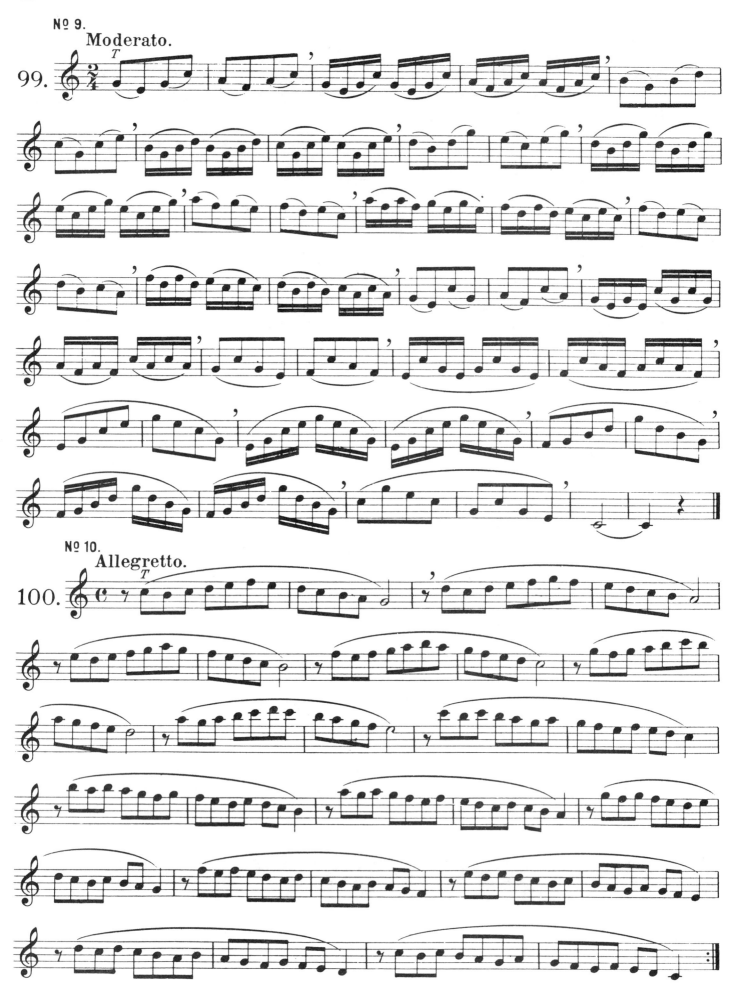

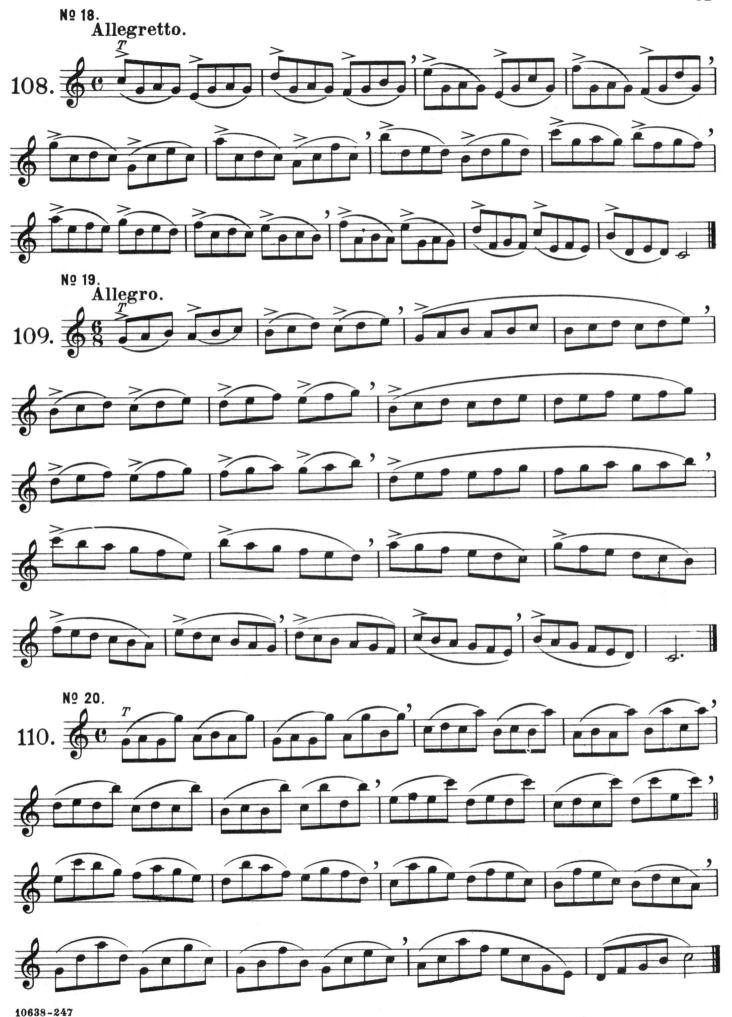

№ 18.
Allegretto.
108.

№ 19.
Allegro.
109.

№ 20.
110.

Eighteen Exercises in articulation.

10638-247

Preparatory Exercises on the High Notes.

Thirds.

Fourths.

Fifths.

Sixths.

Sevenths.

Octaves.

Chromatic Scale of the Saxophone.

Ordinary System.

PAUL de VILLE.

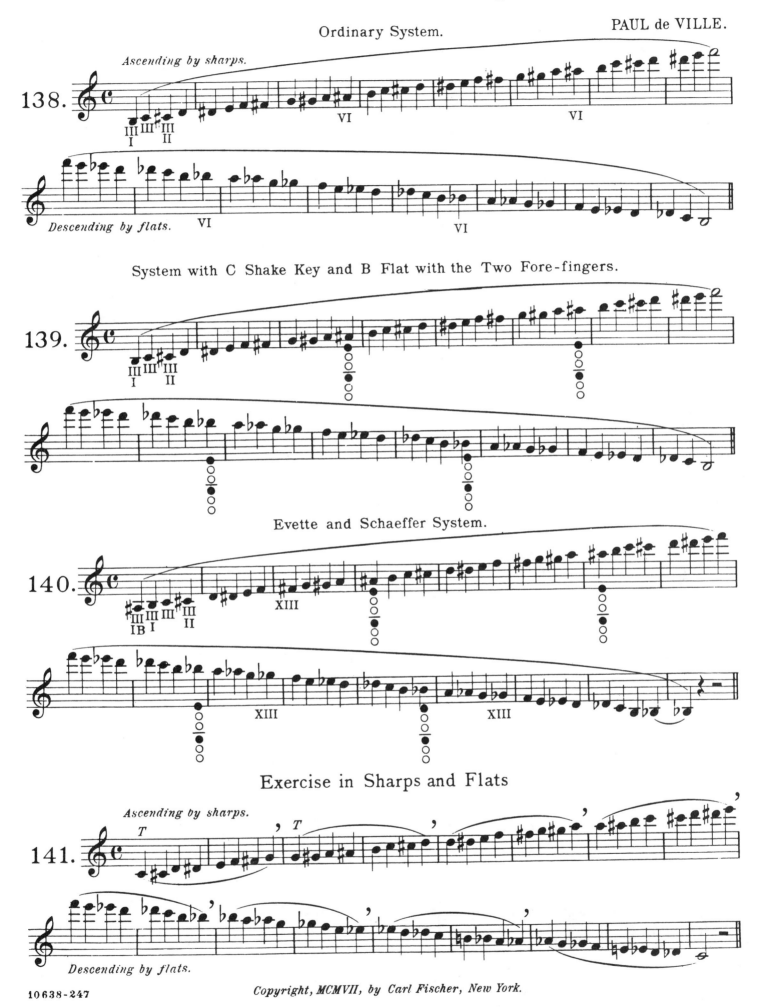

Exercise in Sharps and Flats

Major and Minor Scales in all Keys.

A thorough knowledge of the scales in all keys is most important; the ability to perform them all with equal facility is an absolute requisite to a really good performer.

Every scale should therefore be studied in the following manner: Commence by playing it slowly at first; repeat it many times and at each repetition increase the time slightly. In the keys with several sharps or flats, more especially in those the signatures of which consist of four or more accidentals, the fingering of some intervals is difficult, on account of the mechanism of the instrument. These awkward intervals should be repeated over and over again until an easy mastery over them is secured. No pupil should rest satisfied as long as he finds any interval of a scale a stumblingblock to its easy and perfectly smooth execution.

Rapid tonguing *(staccato)* is very difficult, and can only be acquired by patiently exercising the tongue, making it a point to increase its flexibility by daily practice.

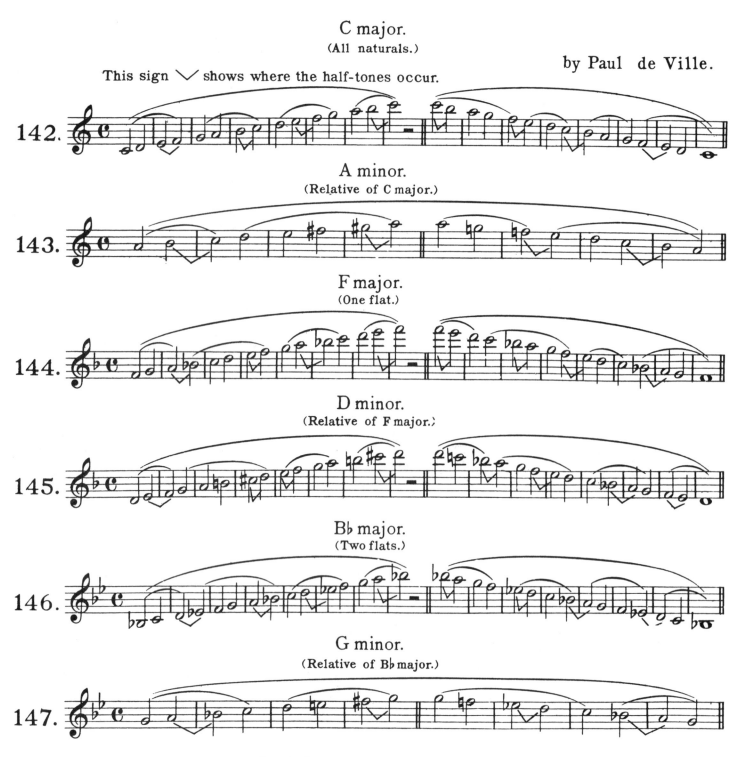

C major.
(All naturals.)

by Paul de Ville.

This sign ⌄ shows where the half-tones occur.

142.

A minor.
(Relative of C major.)

143.

F major.
(One flat.)

144.

D minor.
(Relative of F major.)

145.

B♭ major.
(Two flats.)

146.

G minor.
(Relative of B♭ major.)

147.

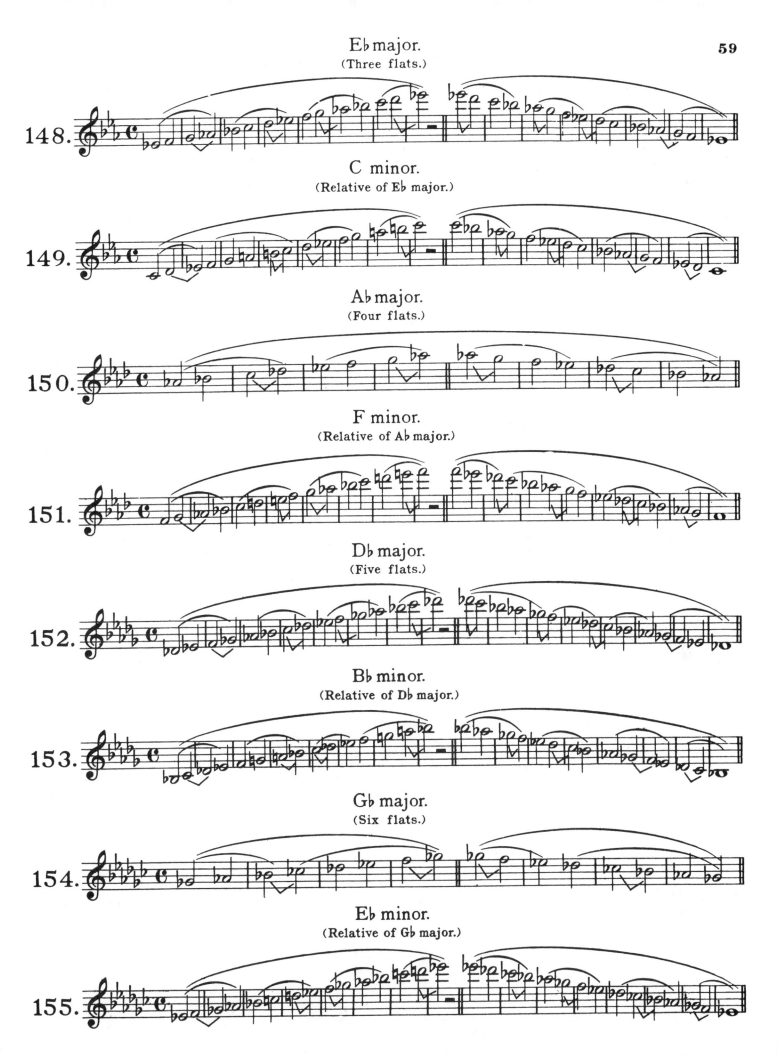

Eb major.
(Three flats.)

148.

C minor.
(Relative of Eb major.)

149.

Ab major.
(Four flats.)

150.

F minor.
(Relative of Ab major.)

151.

Db major.
(Five flats.)

152.

Bb minor.
(Relative of Db major.)

153.

Gb major.
(Six flats.)

154.

Eb minor.
(Relative of Gb major.)

155.

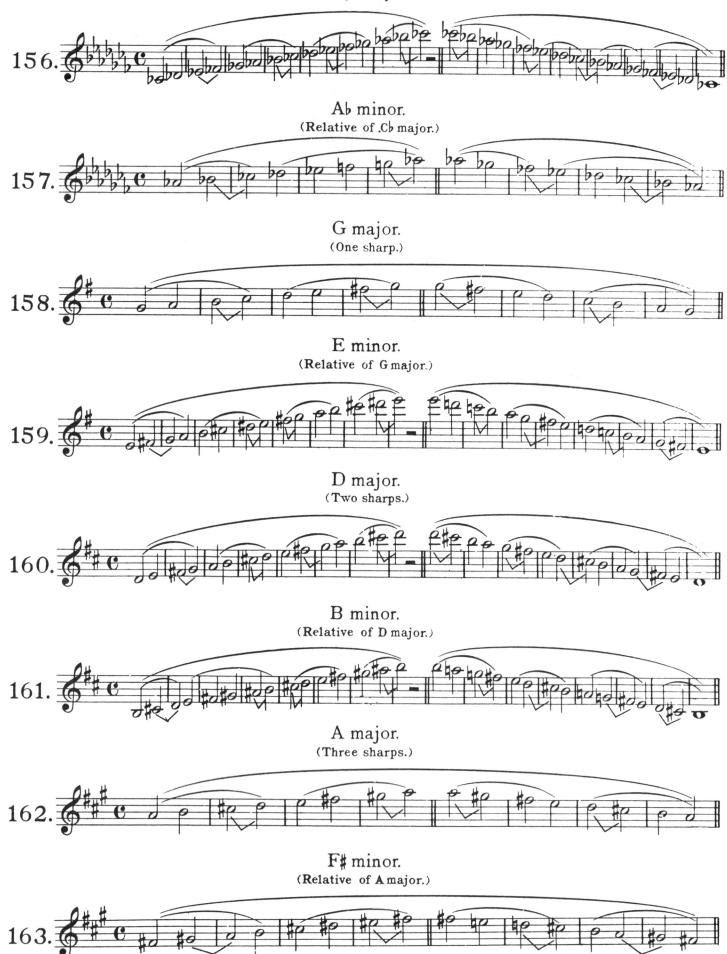

E major.
(Four sharps.)

C# minor.
(Relative of E major.)

B major.
(Five sharps.)

G# minor.
(Relative of B major.)

F# major.
(Six sharps.)

D# minor.
(Relative of F# major.)

C# major.
(Seven sharps, all notes sharp.)

A# minor.
(Relative of C# major.)

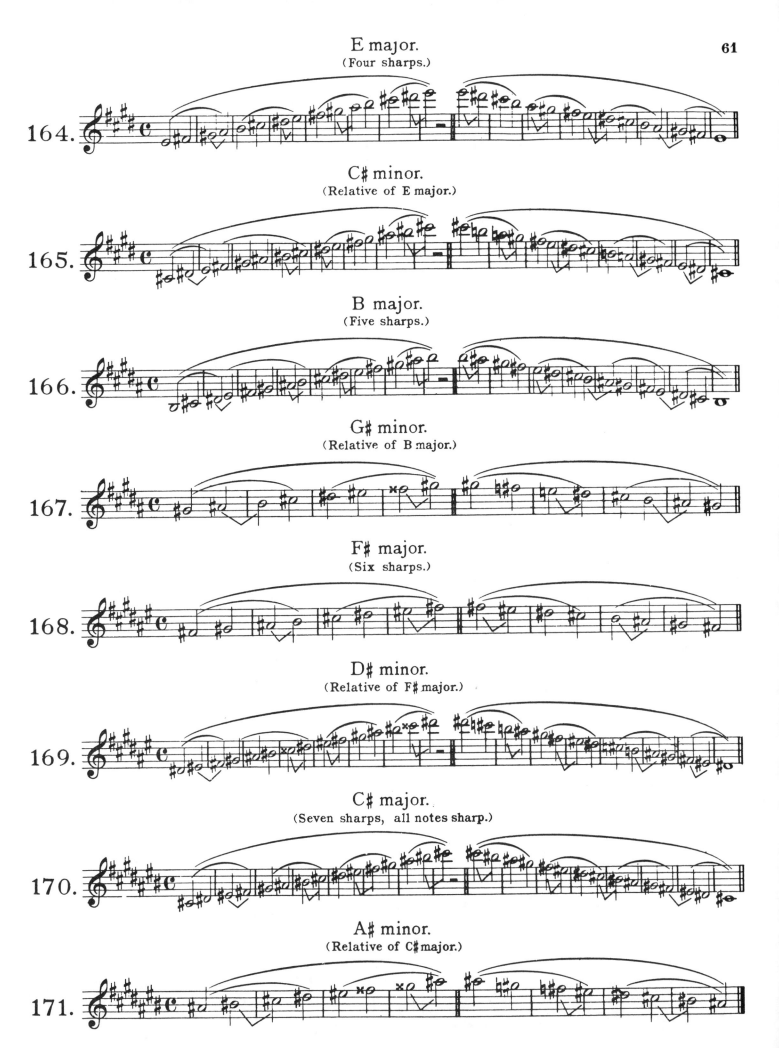

Major and Minor Chords in the Keys most used.

Sixty Exercises of Mechanism.

The exercises of mechanism have for their object the formation of the fingering by habituating each finger to act separately or simultaneously.

By these exercises may be acquired that equality of fingering and that purity of tone which are the finest qualities of an Instrumentalist.

In the following exercises the student must accentuate the sound upon the first note of each division of the bar.

Each bar or each sketch should be played eight or ten times and as a finish play the note after the dotted double bar.

All the notes should be slurred, ascending passages played *crescendo,* descending passages *diminuendo.* (See exercises on Shading, pages 29 and 30).

Take breath after the first note in the bar.

Fifty Exercises from low B♭ to F above the staff.

Saxophone

By A. MAYEUR.

Revised by Paul de Ville.

№ 17.

№ 18.

Take F♯ or G♭ with the key XIII; *improved fingering. (Evette and Schaeffer System.)*

F♯ plate № 5.

G♭-key XIII.

№ 19.

F♯ plate № 5.

Nº 20.

F# plate Nº 5, keep the key G# Nº V open. *(Evette and Schaeffer System.)*

Keep the C#-key closed.

Keep the C#-key closed.

F#-key XIII.

F#-key XIII.

Nº 21.

Keep the Ab-key open. *(Evette and Schaeffer System.)*

Nº 22.

№ 23.

Keep the G♯-key open. F♯ with plate № 5.

Fingering of A♯ or B♭: VI   1st Fingering.   2nd Fingering.   3rd Fingering.   4th Fingering.

№ 24.

Take B♭ 1st fingering with key VI or the 4th fingering (1st finger left hand stretched on the plate 1bis, the plates № 1 and 1bis closed.) *Evette and Schaeffer System.*

B♭ with 1st fingering or with 4th fingering.

B♭ 1st fingering.

№ 25.

B♭ 2nd fingering, keep the plate F № 4 closed.

B♭ 1st fingering.

№ 26.

A# or Bb 3rd fingering, keep the plate F# or Gb № 5 closed.

A# 3rd fingering and keep G# open.

№ 27.

Bb or A# 4th fingering.

Bb 4th fingering.

Keep the Ab-key open.

Bb 4th fingering.

Bb 4th fingering, keep the Ab-key open.

No. 28.
A# 2nd fingering.

No. 29.

Take C with the key VI B.

A# 2nd fingering.

C with the key VI B.

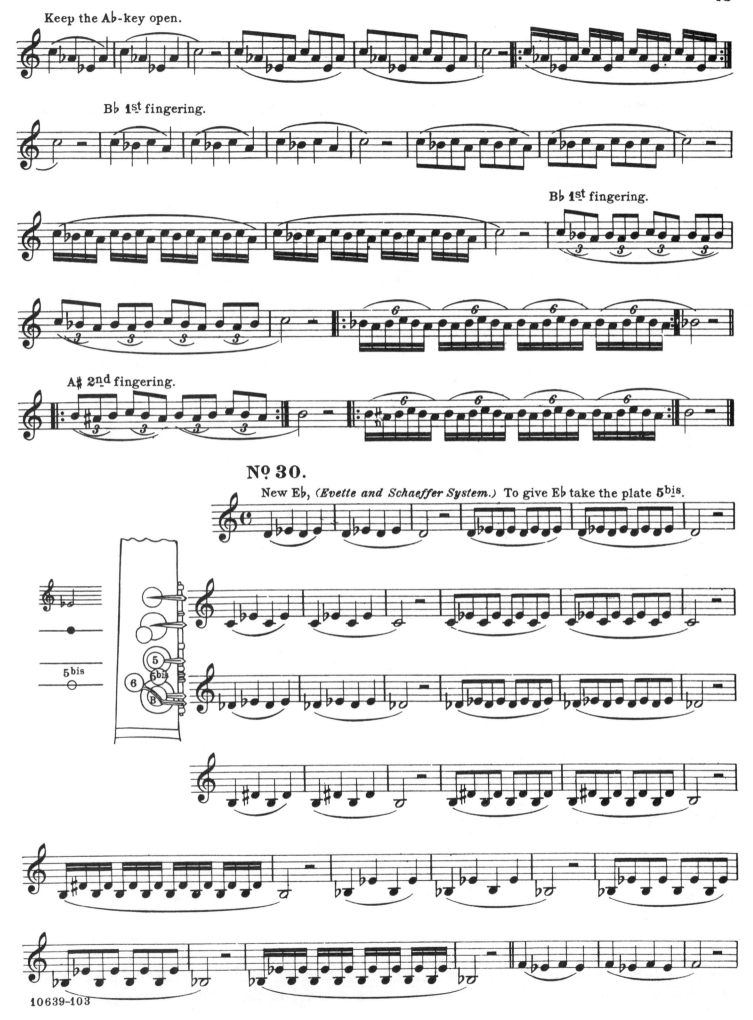

Keep the Ab-key open.

Bb 1st fingering.

Bb 1st fingering.

A# 2nd fingering.

Nº 30.

New Eb, (*Evette and Schaeffer System.*) To give Eb take the plate 5bis.

5bis

76

Keep Ab open.

Keep the Db key open.

Bb 4th fingering.

Keep the Ab key open.

Bb 4th fingering and keep the Db open.

Nº 31.

Bb 1st fingering.

A# 2nd fingering.

10639-103

A# 3rd fingering and keep the G# open.

A# 3rd fingering and keep the F# plate closed.

Nº 32.

Nº 33.

№ 34.

Keep Eb and Bb 2nd or 4th fingering.

Bb 1st fingering.

Bb 4th fingering.

Keep Ab open.

Keep Ab and Eb always open.

Keep Ab open.

Bb **2nd** fingering.

Keep Ab open.

Keep Bb **2nd** fingering.

Nº 37.
Gb key XIII.

A# **3rd** fingering and keep the F# closed

№ 40.

Keep G# open.

Keep G# open.

No 41.

No 42.
Bb 3rd fingering, keep Gb and Eb open.

No 43.
Bb 4th fingering. (*Evette and Schaeffer Sytem.*)

4th fingering Bb.

Bb 4th fingering, keep Ab open.

Nº 44.

C key VI B.

Keep G♯ open.

C key VI B.

C key VI B.

Nº 45.

Keep G# open.

Keep G# open.

No. 46.

For the Sixteenth-notes keep the C plate closed and take the D♮ with the key IX.

No. 47.

Keep B♭ 2nd fingering.

Keep B♭ 4th fingering.

B♭ always 4th fingering.

№ 48.

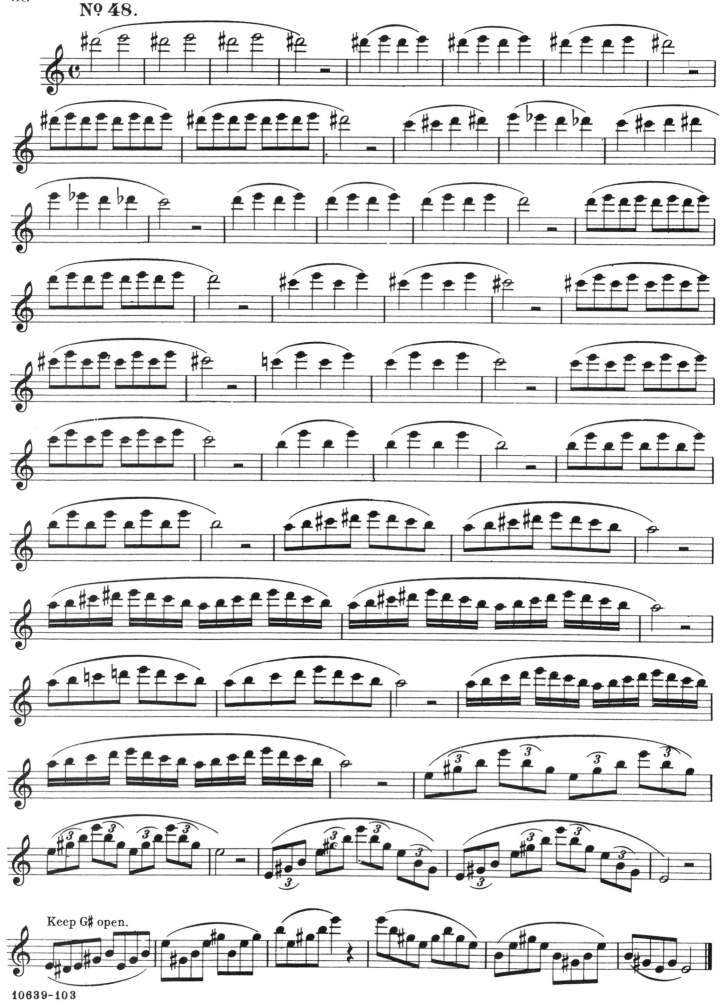

№ 49.

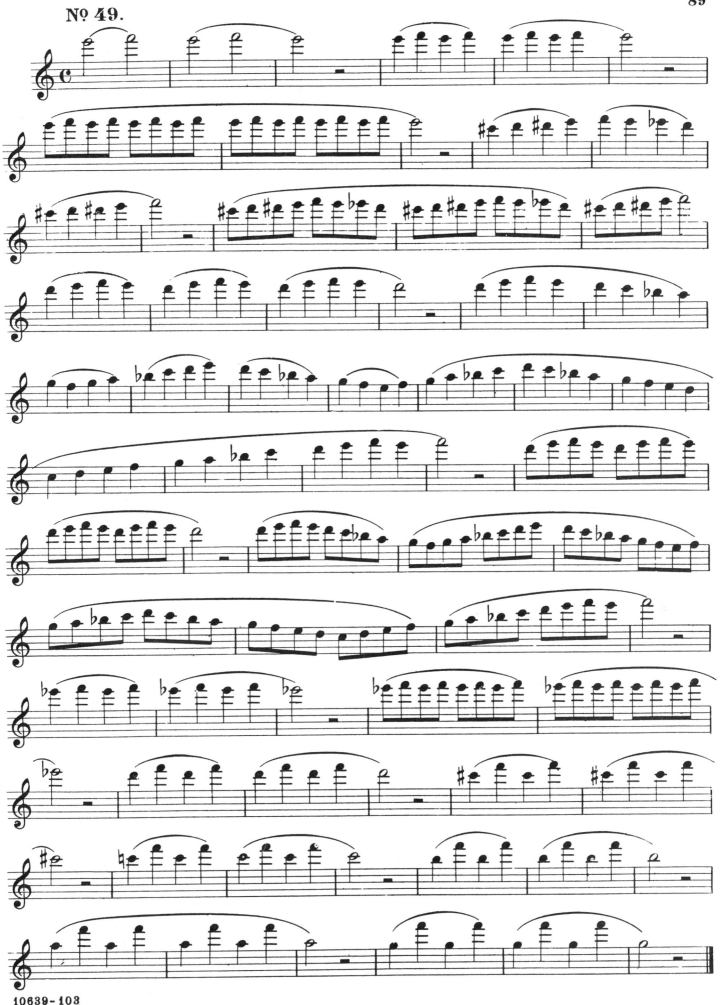

Exercises for the new key of E♮ and F above the staff.

Evette and Schaeffer System.

No 50.

Twenty-one Exercises on Detached Notes,
in different Keys.

Key of C.

Key of F.

Key of Bb.

96

10638-247

Twenty-seven Exercises for gaining execution
in the different Keys.

J. A. KAPPEY.
Edited by PAUL de VILLE.

A minor.

D minor.

G minor.

D♯ minor.

21.

D♭ major.

22.

Allegretto.

26.

107

Three Exercises on Staccato.

Practise at first slowly, then quicken the time till they can be played Allegro.

Allegretto.

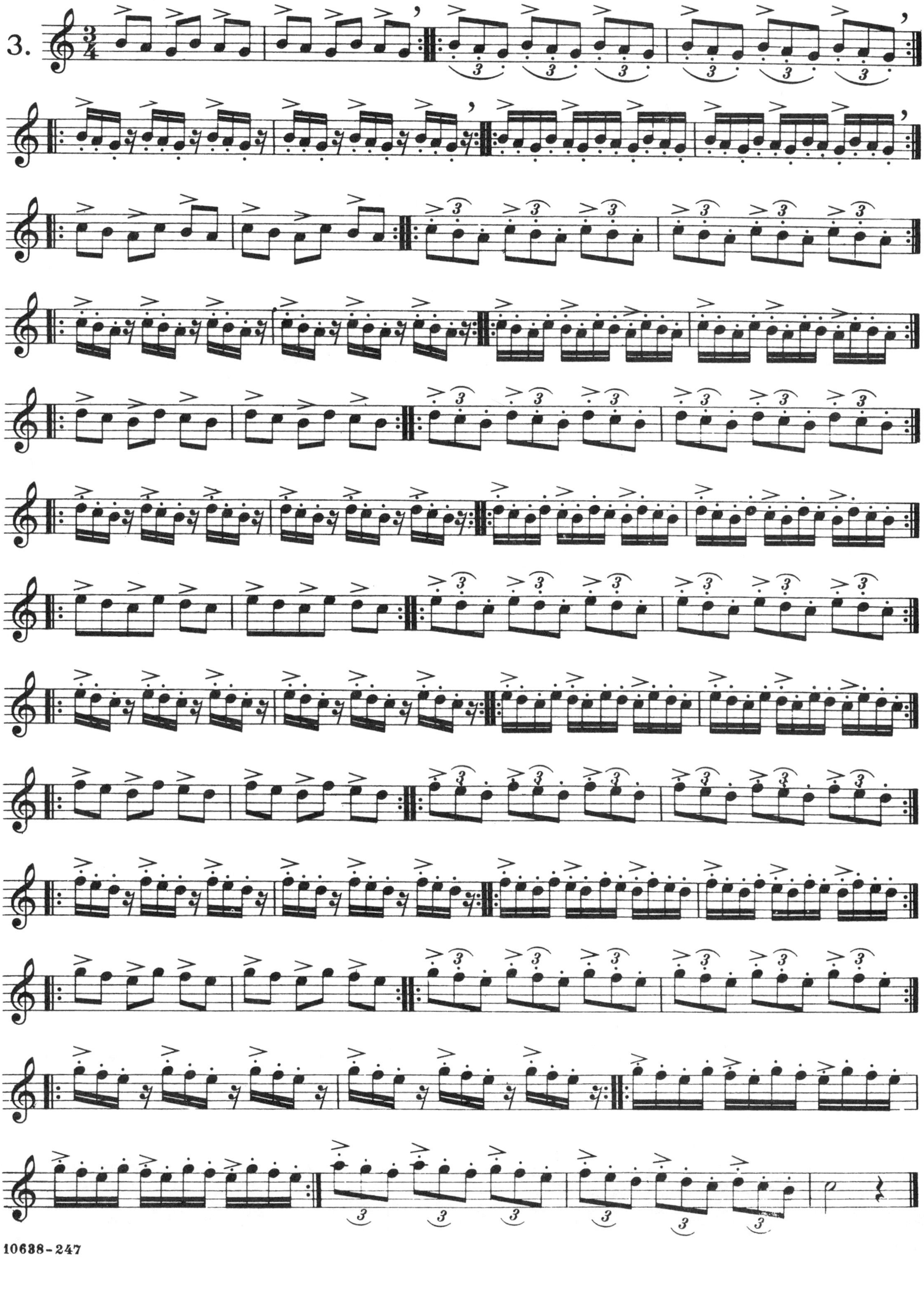

Grace-notes and Embellishments.

These are of considerable variety, and consist of *simple grace-notes,* (appoggiatura), *double grace-notes,* (double appoggiaturas); *the turn,* (Gruppetto) indicated by the sign ∾ or ⸮ and consisting of three or four notes of a fixed order, and gruppettos of more than four notes. With referance to the longer ornamental phrases, or Gruppettos, it is necessary to state that the the manner of writing them has gradually undergone great alteration. Formerly the simple Melody was written in full notes, and all the embellishments in half-sized ones, (called by the general name of: grace notes); but in our time the composers prefer to write embellishments in full notes, thus making them an integral part of the Melody.

A further ornament is the short, or *passing Shake,* (Mordente,) indicated: ᷉, — and the full *Shake,* or Trill, indicated thus: *tr,* an abbreviation of the Italian word "Trillo".

Lastly there is the *Cadenza,* an elaborate ornamental phrase, mostly performed as a grand final climax to bravura pieces. In ancient music the Cadenza was left to the inventive genius of the singer or instrumental performer, and merely indicated thus: ; but at present composers prefer to write the Cadenzas in full.

As a rule ornaments should not be added by a performer except where they are indicated by the Composer. — Some ordinary performers are under the delusion that it "shows off" a player if he can "beautify" a piece with grace-notes and shakes, and trembling breath, and other means. This is offensive to good musical taste, and amounts to mere vulgarity. — But when embellishments are introduced at the *right place,* and performed by an *"artist,"* their style of execution furnishes a criterion for the estimate of the artist's schooling and delicacy of feeling.

Examples.

Grace-note, or Appoggiatura.

The most frequent "Appoggiatura," (literally "jammed note,") is written thus ♪, with an oblique stroke through stem and hook.

This is invariably played very quickly.

But there are cases, more especially in ancient music, where the grace-note has *no stroke* through the stem. These are to be played as if they were written in full notes, the time value of which is to be taken from the note to which it is slurred. Per example, if the grace-notes in the preceding exercise had no strokes through the stems ✱)

Appoggiaturas of various durations.

Exercise.

The "Double Appoggiatura" or Double Grace-note.

Is always performed rapidly, and its value is deducted from the preceding note, so that the following note falls exactly upon the time-beat.

Exercises.

Exercise.

The "Turn," (Gruppetto).

May be of three, four, or even five notes, upwards or down, written in full or by the signs ∾ (upwards) or ∾ (down). Any accidental over or under the sign, ♮ ♭ ♯ ♮, indicates that the highest or lowest note of the turn should be either ♯ or ♮, as indicated. Its time-value is always taken from the preceding note.

Andantino.

When the Turn is between similar notes, it always consists of three notes.

When it is placed between ascending notes, it consists of four notes. (Upward turn.)

When it stands between descending notes, it con-

sists of four notes, the first of which is the lowest, and the third the highest. (Downward turn.)

It must, however, be remarked that there is no *absolute* rule, and it depends upon the artistic conception of the performer, whether he prefers the upward or downward execution of an indicated turn.

The preceding exercise is to be performed in the following manner:

Andantino.

Gruppettos of more than four notes are not so frequent, but examples by Rossini and other composers will be found in operatic melodies, and also some Cadenzas.

The Shake.
(Trill.)

This is indicated by the sign *tr*, an abbreviation of the Italian word: Trillo, (trill,) and consists of a rapid alternation of the note over which the sign *tr* is placed, with the next note above.

The shake may consist of a full tone, or a semitone, according to the key of the piece, and the position of the note in the scale of the key. Shakes present little trouble if they are executed with the first or second finger; but much greater difficulty is experienced if they are to be done by the third, and more so with the fourth or little finger. This is due to the anatomical construction of the hand; the ability to execute a good shake with the latter two fingers can only be acquired by persevering exercise, and great trouble has to be taken to equalise the rapidity of all fingers; a few shakes have even to be performed by the thumb. Every shake must be practised at first slowly, and the rapidity of the finger should, in the daily exercises be increased gradually, until the required speed is attained. The close or end of a shake should consist of a turn.

Table of Shakes.

PAUL de VILLE.

Keep the D ♯ opened.

Keep the E ♭ opened and move together the plates Nos. 5 and 6.

Keep the F ♮ and move the key XIII.

10639-108

Keep the G♯ opened and move
the plate of F♯

Keep G♯ opened.

Two ways to shake A♭ with B♭.
1st keep the A♭ opened and the left hand plates closed
and move the key VI.
2nd take the new B♭ *(Evette and Schaeffer System)* keep the
A♭ opened and move together the plates N°2 and 3 of
the left hand.

Keep the plate of B and move
the plate of F♮.

Keep the plate of C closed, the key VI
being opened and move the plate N°1
left hand

The C with the key VIbis

Keep the plate of C closed and move the key IX.

All the plates opened and move the key № VIII.

Move together the keys VIII and IX.

Keep the key of D and move the key of E♮.

You can play a succession or chain of shakes up or down without ending, keeping the end for the last shake of the succession or chain.

Example

You can play a succession or chain of shakes up, in adding an end at each shake.

Example.

The Mordent, or Passing Shake.

A brief shake, indicated thus ᨓ, consists of a few rapid alternations of the note with the one next a-bove it, having neither beginning nor end. They occur mostly in rapid movements.

Examples.

Exercises on Shakes.

Fifteen Cadenzas.

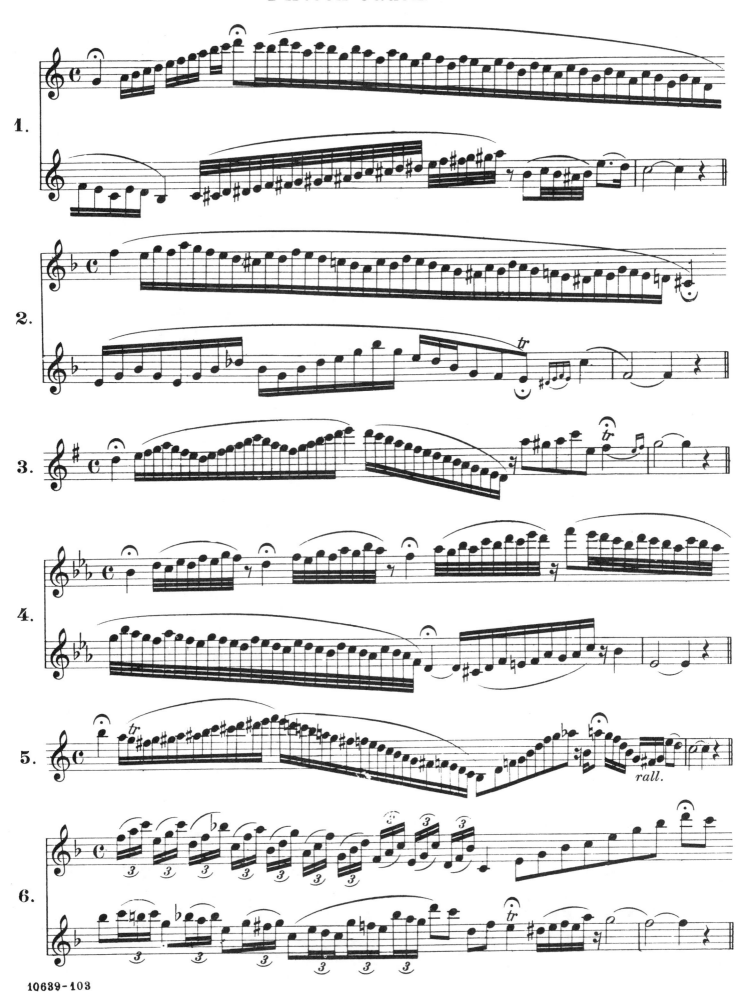

Fantaisie on Norma.

Trill F sharp with G sharp.

Introduction of the Adagio of the pathetic sonata of Beethoven.

Andante.

2.

Andante et lentement.

3.

Tempo

ritard.

Tempo

Ten Duets
For Two E♭ or Two B♭ Saxophones.

A. MAYEUR.
Revised by Paul de Ville.

Allegro moderato.

HAYDN

Allegro moderato.

5.

Andante moderato.

6.

Allegretto.

8.

Six Duets
for Two E♭ or Two B♭ Saxophones.

N⁰ 1.

H. KLOSÉ.
Revised by Paul de Ville.

Moderato.

№ 2.

Allegro non troppo.

№ 3.
Andantino.

No 4.
Moderato.

№ 5.

Andante.

№ 6.
Moderato.

Exercises on Eighth Notes and Sixteenth Notes.

Moderato.

5.

Exercises on Dotted Eighth Notes and Sixteenth Notes.

1.

2.

Exercise with Sixteenth-note Rests.

Exercise on Dotted Sixteenth-notes and Thirty-second-notes.

Exercise with Thirty-second-note Rests.

Exercises on Triplets.

1.

Forty Exercises on the Slurred and Detached Notes.

for Saxophone

A. MAYEUR.

Edited by Paul de Ville.

Two slurred and two detached.

Two detached and two slurred.

3.

Three slurred and one detached.

Slurred in groups of two. (Play evenly the two notes.)

6.

7.

Slurred in groups of four.

8.

One detached and three slurred.
(The first note should be well marked, and separated.)

9.

One detached, two slurred and one detached.

10.

Reversed slur.
(Accent the first note of the slur.)

11.

Slurred in groups of two.

dim.

172

Three slurred and one detached.

15.

One detached and three slurred.
(The first note should be well marked and separated.)

16.

ritard.

10638-247

Slurred three and detached three.

Slurred two and detached two.

Slurred three and detached five.

Detached one and Slurred three.

32.

Slurred two and detached six.

Slurred two and detached two.

33.

34.

Seventeen Exercises on Syncopation.

Syncopation between two Eights.
The note preceding the syncopation must be separated, and the quarter well marked.

Three Syncopated Notes preceding a Half-note.

Syncopated Slurs.

The accent must <u>not</u> be made by the throat, but by the action of the finger falling like a hammer on the hole

The first eight measures which are slurred should be played with one breath until the rest. But should the movement be two slow, breath can be taken after the quarter-note preceding the syncopation.

Twenty Operatic Melodies
for the study of phrasing and artistic delivery.

Compiled by PAUL de VILLE.

It is difficult to give verbal instructions how to perform in an *artistic* style. The great point consists in delivering a melody as if it were rendered by a great Singer. The student should utilize every opportunity to hear good vocal artists and model his delivery of "Cantabile" pieces after their example. Of course there are many artistic details for an instrumentalist which lie outside the vocal art, and ought to be imitated from the performances of the best instrumental performers.

Especial care should be taken with the articulation; the tongue must touch the reed in staccato passages at the very tip, crisp and clear. If the articulation is produced by the tongue covering too much of the reed, the tone will be forced and vulgar. The dynamic shadings should be clearly brought out, without resorting to extremes; vibrating the breath ought to be strictly avoided, and the "roulades" (long vocal passages) must be fingered with the greatest precision, so that no break occurs.

Norma.

Cavatina "Il Pirata."

La Traviata.

VERDI.

Martha.

FLOTOW.

Il Trovatore.

Andante.

VERDI.

N⁰ 5.

Ah! Che La Morte.

Andante.

VERDI.

N⁰ 6.

La Sonnambula.

Allegro moderato.

BELLINI.

N⁰ 7.

Martha.

Giulio Cesare.

HÄNDEL.

Lucia di Lammermoor.

DONIZETTI.

L' Ebreo.

Tempo di Polacca.

G. APOLLONI.

No 13.

Der Förster.

BALLADE.
Larghetto.

FLOTOW.

No 14.

Cadenza ad lib.

Belisario.

RECITATIV.
Andante.

ROSSINI.

No 15.

ad lib.

Cadenza

190

Moderato.

piu mosso

Cadenza ad lib.

10638-247

La Gazza Ladra.

Allegro. (♩. = 60)

ROSSINI.

Nº 16.

La Sonnambula.

BELLINI.

Ernani.

Allegro con brio.

VERDI.

Nº 18.

The Huguenots.

MEYERBEER.

Air from Masaniello.

AUBER.

Exercises for the new fingering
of the improved B♭, B♮ and C♯ Keys.

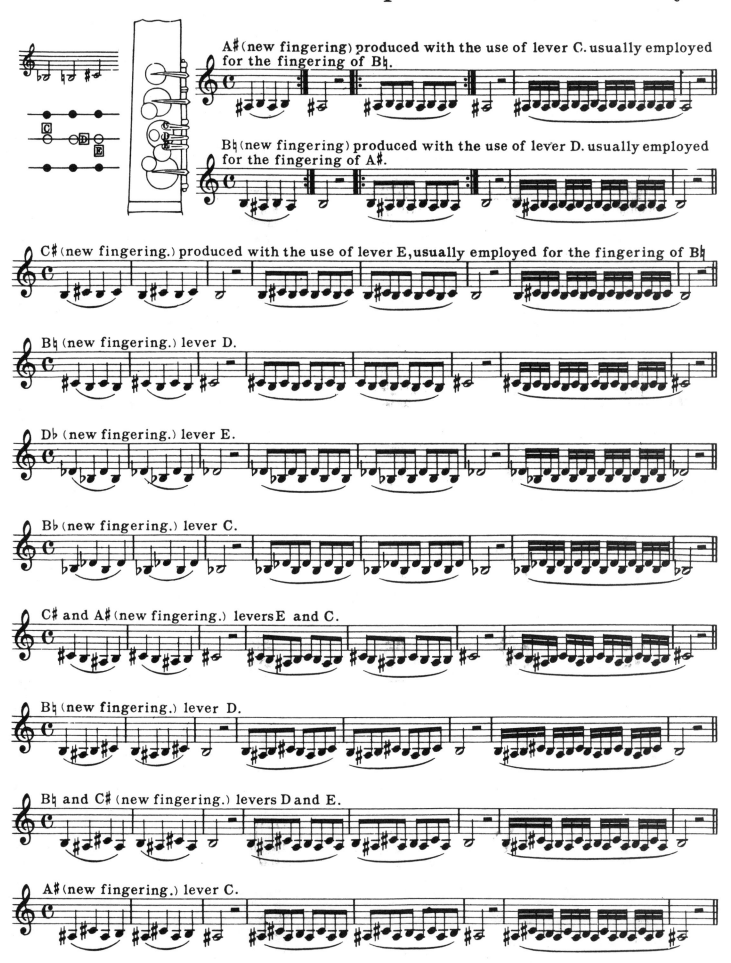

A♯ (new fingering) produced with the use of lever C. usually employed for the fingering of B♮.

B♮ (new fingering) produced with the use of lever D. usually employed for the fingering of A♯.

C♯ (new fingering.) produced with the use of lever E, usually employed for the fingering of B♮

B♮ (new fingering.) lever D.

D♭ (new fingering.) lever E.

B♭ (new fingering.) lever C.

C♯ and A♯ (new fingering.) levers E and C.

B♮ (new fingering.) lever D.

B♮ and C♯ (new fingering.) levers D and E.

A♯ (new fingering.) lever C.

Carl Fischer New York.

Db (new fingering.) lever E. the Bb with the **4**th finger and attention to the open Ab *(Evette and Schaeffer System.)*

C# (new fingering.) lever E.

B♮ (new fingering.) lever D.

B♮ and C# (new fingering.) levers D and E.

B♮ (new fingering.) lever D.

Db (new fingering.) lever E.

Bb (new fingering.) lever C.

Bb medium marked with the **4**th finger, attention to the open Ab *(Evette and Schaeffer System)*
The low Bb (new fingering.)

Progressive Major and Minor Scales, and Exercises.

For Saxophone.

PAUL de VILLE.

Copyright, MCMXI, by Carl Fischer, New York.

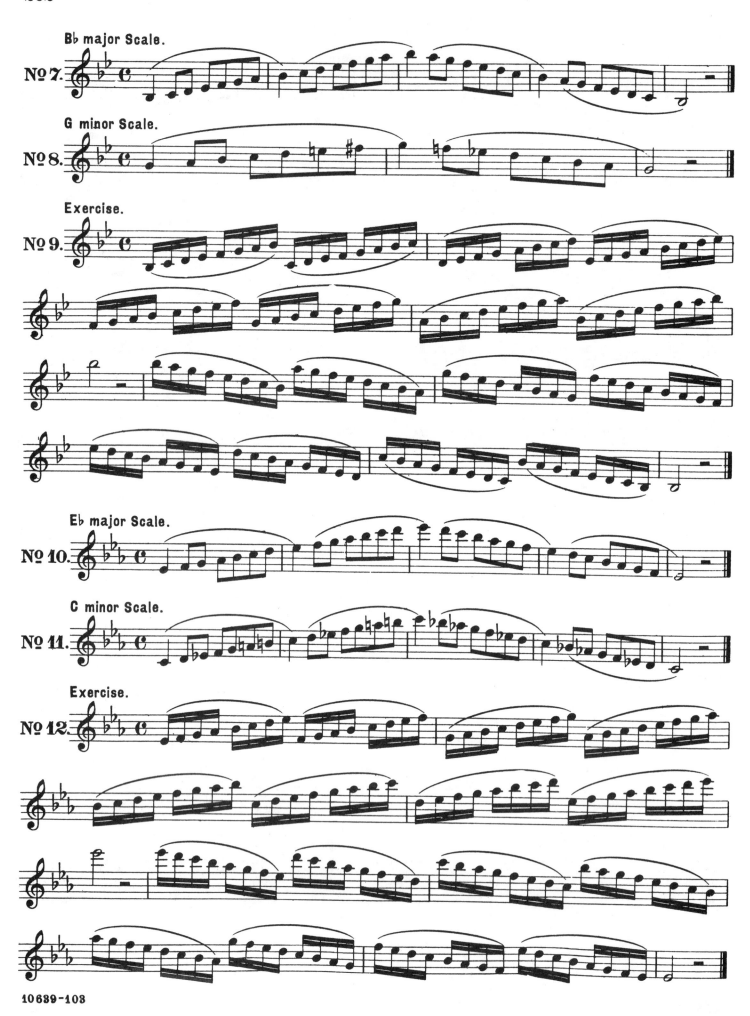

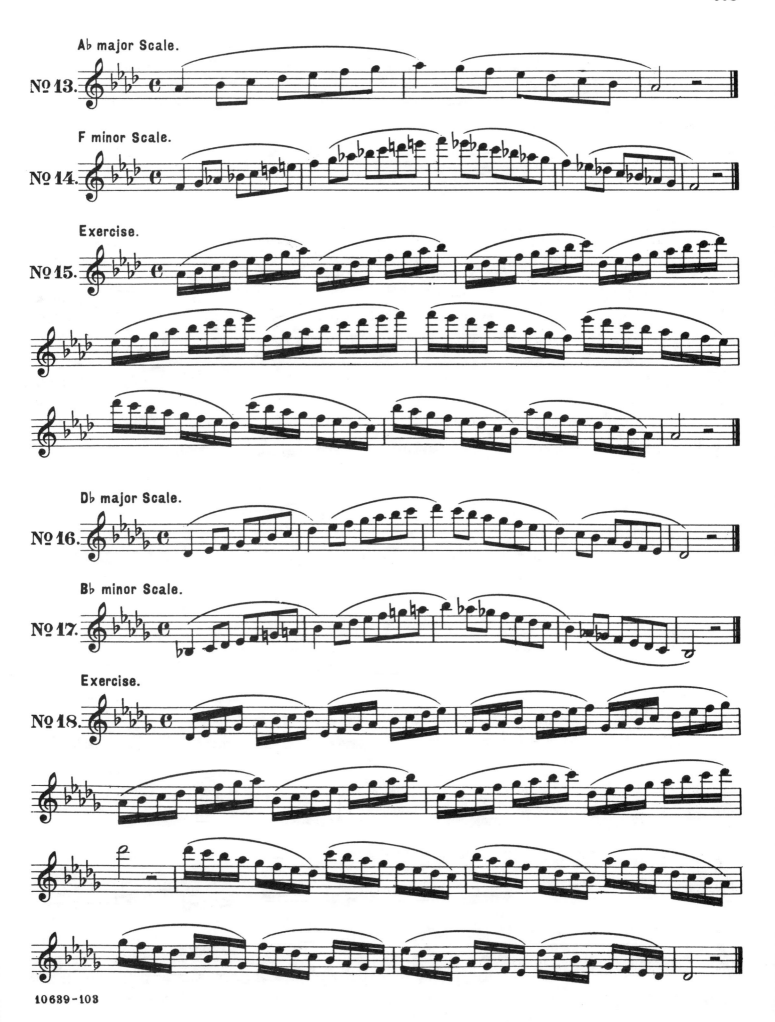

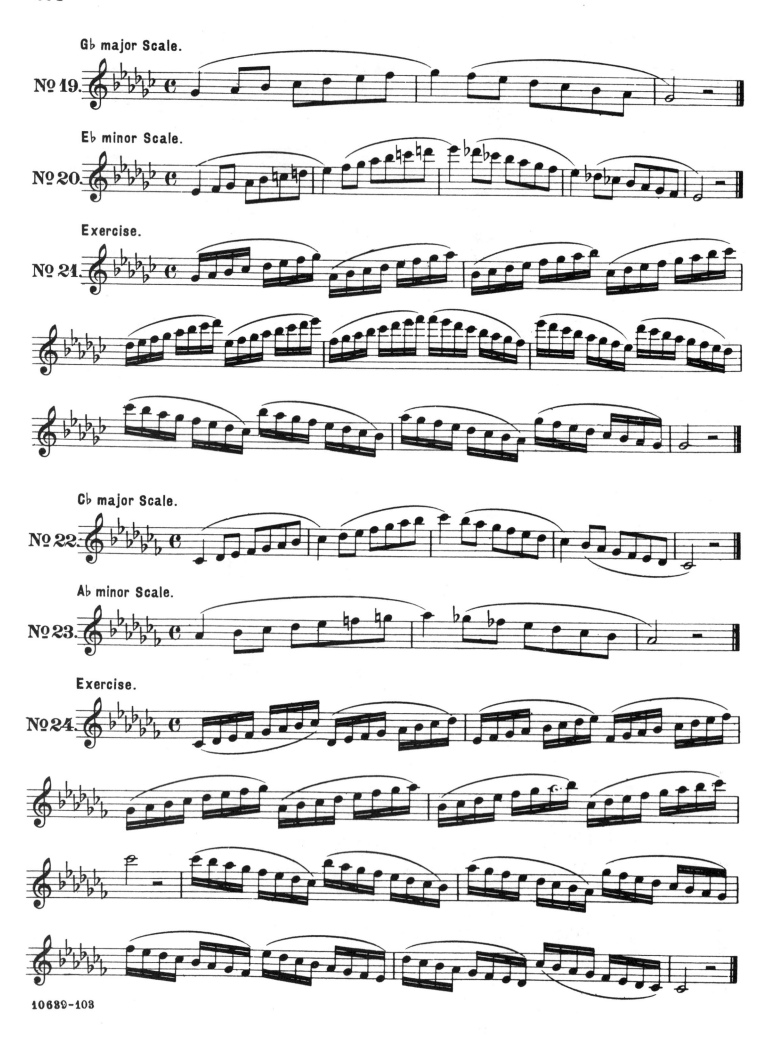

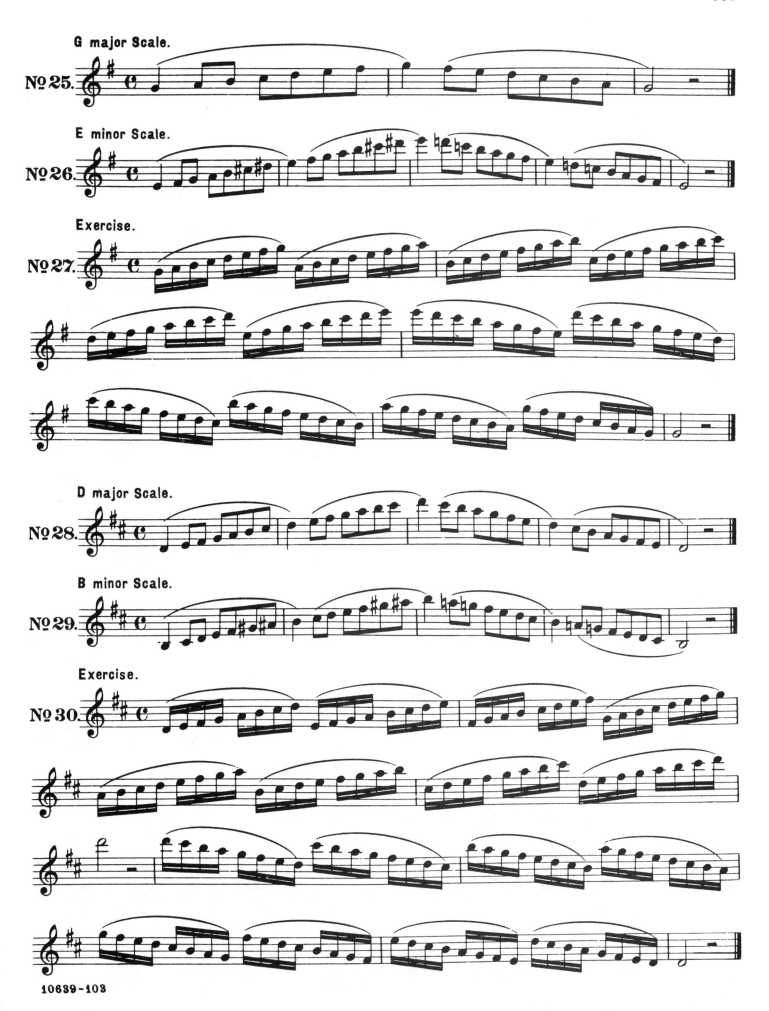

Interval Exercises on the Major and Minor Scales.

210.

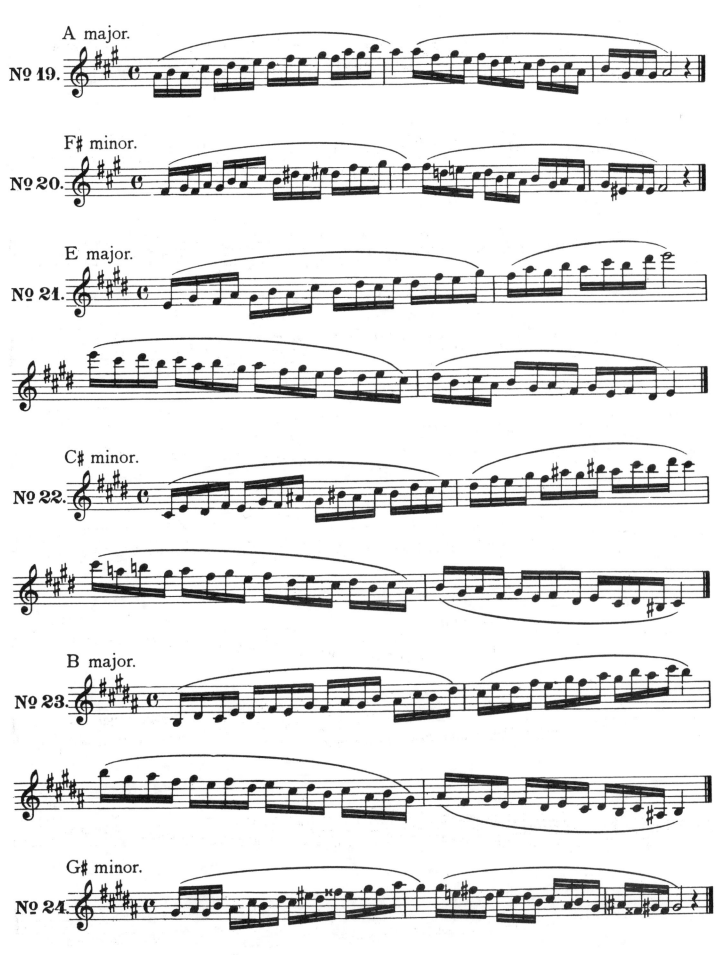

Studies on the Major and Minor Chords.

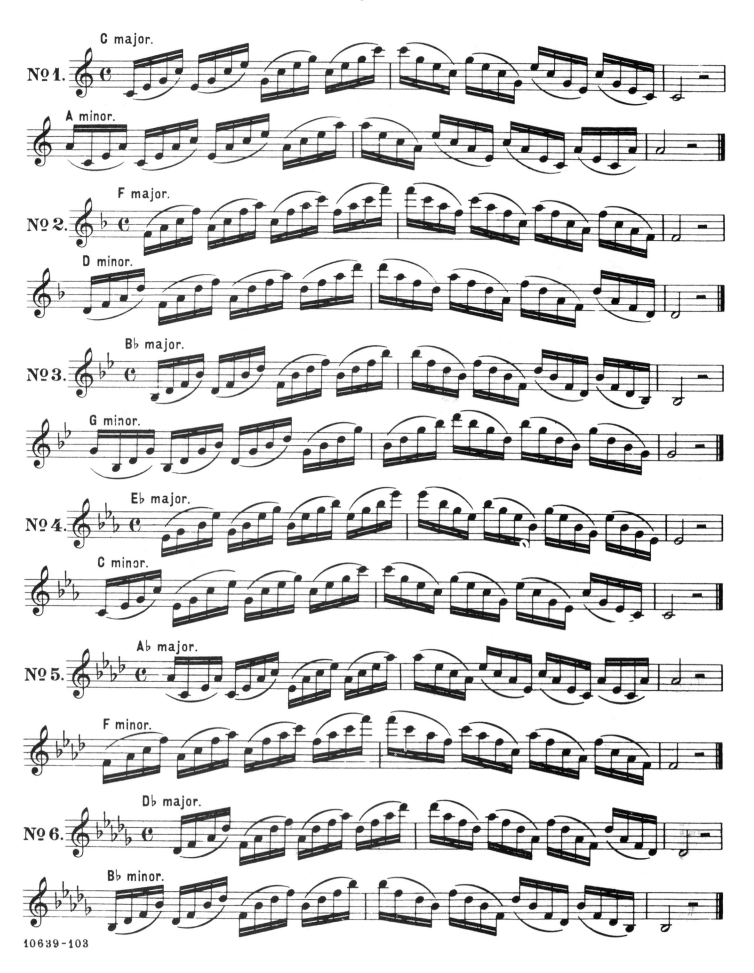

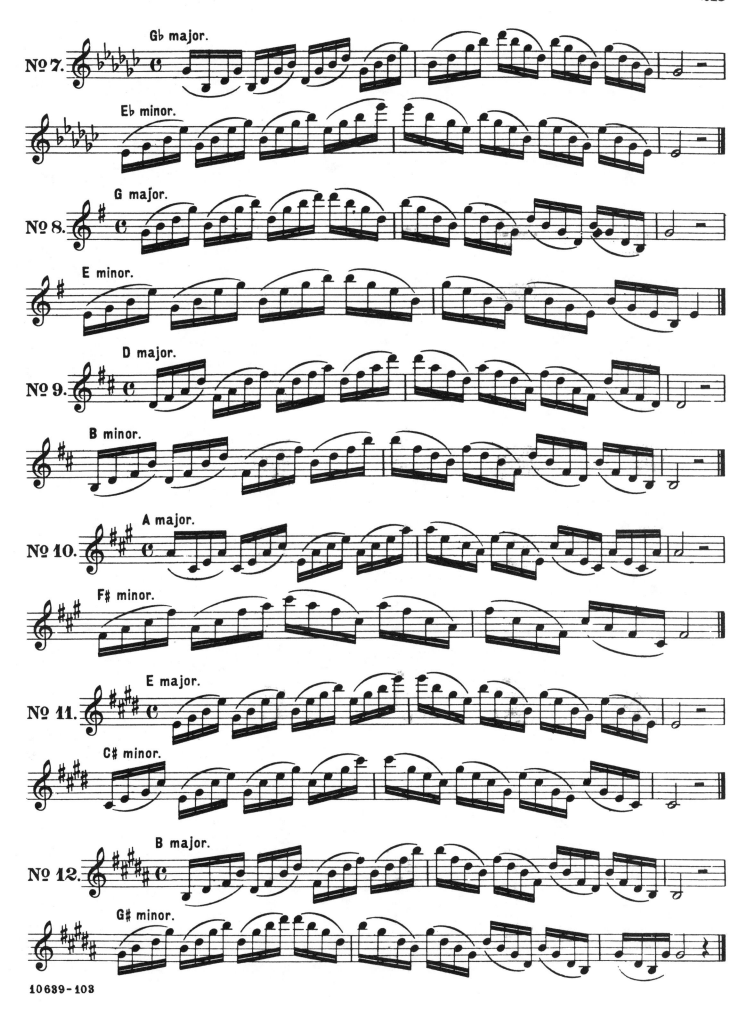

Exercise on the Chords of the Dominant Seventh.

Exercise on different Diminished Sevenths.

Exercise on the Succession of four Diminished Sevenths.

Ten Studies on appeggios in different Major Keys.

Chromatic Exercises.

Study these exercises slowly.

EIGHT FANTASIAS.

FANTASIA ON DON GIOVANNI.

H. Lazarus.
Revised by Paul De Vill.
MOZART

Copyright, MCMXI, by Carl Fischer, New York

Introduction.
Moderato.

2.

GERMAN AIR.

GERMAN AIR.

Tempo di Bolero.

eleganza un poco risoluto.

leggiero.

a tempo.

un poco animato.

BOLERO.

BELLINI.

Eleven Progressive Studies.

For Saxophone.

J. A. KAPPEY.
Edited by Paul de Ville.

10638-247

Allegretto.

7.

rall.

Allegro.

8.

Extract from a Clarinet Solo
by G. MÜLLER.

Allegretto moderato.

11.

Theme with Nine Easy Variations.

VAR. III.
Moderato.

The following variations to be practised slowly at first, and increasing the time as the fingering gets easier.

VAR. IV.

VAR. VII.
Alla marcia.

VAR. VIII.
Alla Valse.

rall.

a tempo

VAR. IX.
Alla Polacca.

rall.

f

Theme with Variations.

Twenty Studies.
For Saxophone.

A. MAYEUR.
Revised by Paul de Ville.

Andante.

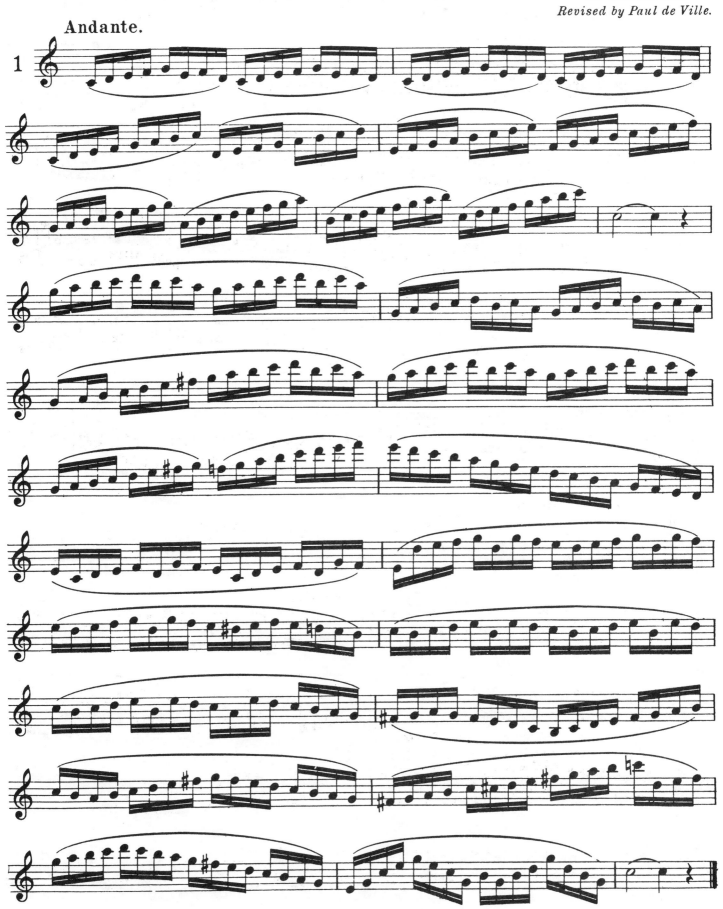

10639-103

Andante.

2.

Andante.

3.

Allegro moderato.

Andante.

9.

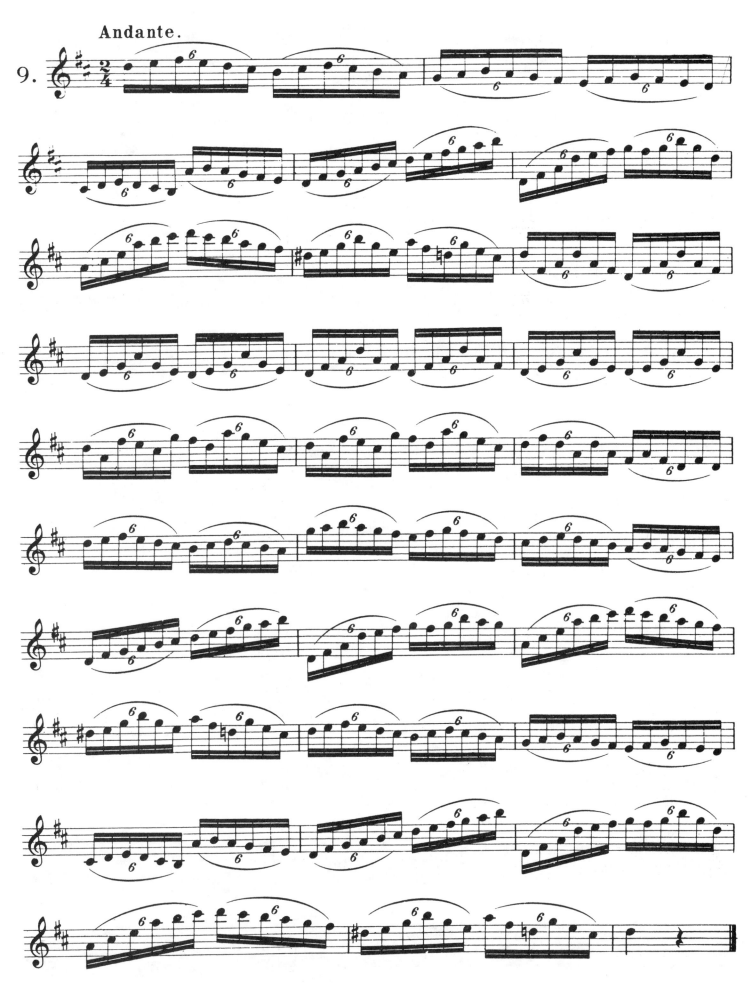

Allegro moderato.

12.

Allegro moderato.

13.

Moderato. Count four beats to a bar.

14.

Allegro moderato.

16.

Allegro moderato.

18.

Allegro moderato.

19.

ted by Paul de Ville.

Henry Lazarus

Vivo.

Moderato.

Allegro non troppo.

7.

Allegro vivace.

8.

Exercises on difficult fingerings.

Vivace.

12.

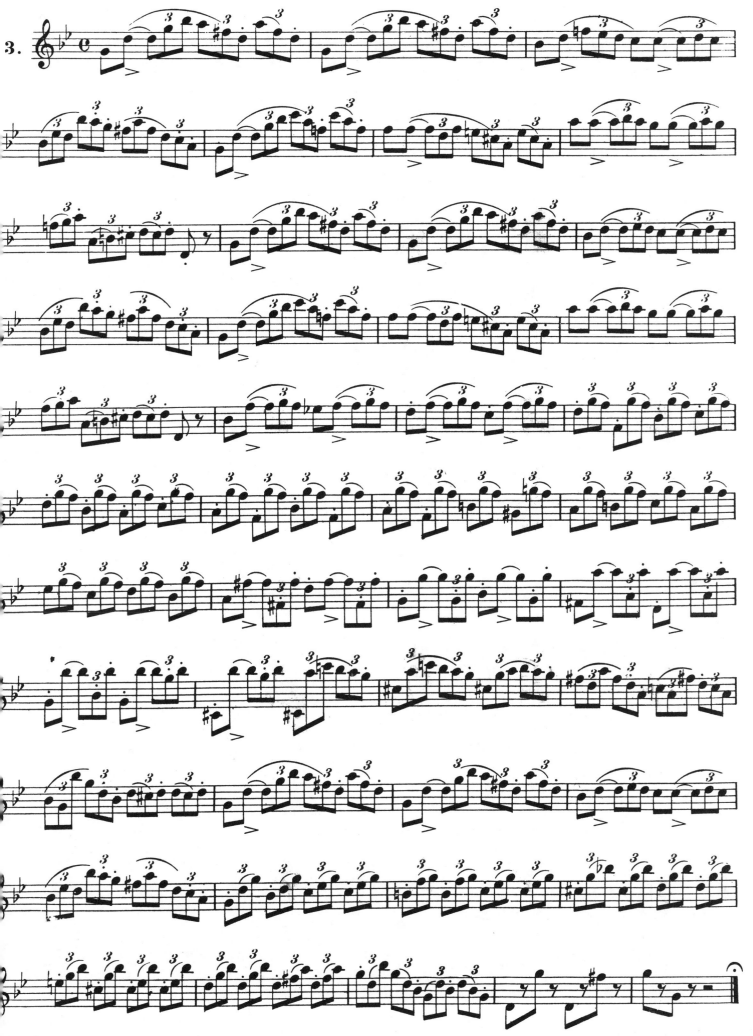

Four Solos.

Cavatine de Zelmire.

INTRODUCTION.
Moderato.

Arranged by
PAUL de VILLE.

1.

Elle est Partie.

Morceau Caracteristique.

H. KLOSÉ

Il Crociato.

Andante quasi Allegretto.

MEYERBEER.

Andante quasi Allegretto.

AIR WITH VARIATIONS.

FROM DONIZETTI'S ELISIRE D'AMORE.

Four Concert Duets

for two E♭ or two B♭ Saxophones.

H. KLOSÉ.
Edited by Paul de Ville.

Moderato non troppo.

Nᵒ 1.

Copyright, MCMXI by Carl Fischer, New York.

Fine.

Allegro giusto.

Andantino sostenuto.

№ 4.

Alto Saxophone.

"Adagio"
Concerto Militaire.

C. KÜHN.
arr. by E. A. Léfèbre.

5319-4

"Serenade."

Eb Alto Saxophone Solo.

FRANZ SCHUBERT.
Trans. by E. A. Lefèbre.

Copyright 1904 by Carl Fischer, New York.

"Give me thy Heart."

Solo for E♭ Alto Saxophone.

E♭ Alto Saxophone.

TRANSCRIPTION
arr. by E. A. Lefèbre

"Ballet Music"

from Ch. Gounod's
"Faust."

Eb Alto Saxophone Solo.

arr. by E. A. LEFÈBRE.

Allegretto mouvement de Valse.

C.R.
8851-3

Berceuse.
(Cradle Song.)

Eb Alto Saxophone Solo.

B. GODARD.
arr. by E. A. Lefebre.

C.R.
8349_5

Eb Alto Saxophone Solo.

Hungarian Dance
No. 5

Eb Alto Saxophone

JOHANNES BRAHMS
Arranged by Ben Conklin

C
25208-6

"CAPRICE-GAVOTTE."

(Solo for Alto Saxophone.)

Alto Saxophone Solo.

E. GILLET.

Transcribed by E. A. Lefebre.

6205-8

Copyright 1900 by Carl Fischer New York.

Alto Saxophone Solo.

"Happy be Thy Dreams."

Air varié

for Piccolo, E♭ Clarinet, E♭ or B♭ Saxophone
Baritone (Trombone) or E♭ Bass.

Solo E♭ Clarinet.
(E♭ Alto Saxophone.)

arr. by Paul de Ville.

And^{te} con moto.

Solo E♭ Clarinet (E♭ Alto Saxophone.)

Cad.

TUTTI.

BLUE BELLS OF SCOTLAND.

Eb Alto Saxophone.
(Solo Eb Clarinet)

Air varié.

Paul de Ville.

Copyright 1891 by Carl Fischer, New York.

La Cinquantaine
(The Golden Wedding)

E♭ Alto Saxophone

GABRIEL P. MARIE
Transcribed by Ben Vereecken

Solo E♭ Clarinet.
and Solo E♭ Alto
Saxophone.

Jennie - Polka.

Solo for Piccolo, E♭ Clarinet, Alto Saxophone,
B♭ Cornet, Baritone or Trombone.

Webb- De Ville.

Solo E♭ Clarinet and Solo E♭ Alto Saxophone.

Sextet
from
"Lucia di Lammermoor"

Eb Alto Saxophone

GAETANO DONIZETTI
Transcribed by Ben Vereecken

25518—5
19911—102

PRACTICE PLANNER

Date	Page	Goals/Comments	Remarks

PRACTICE PLANNER

Date	Page	Goals/Comments	Remarks

Saxophone Quartets

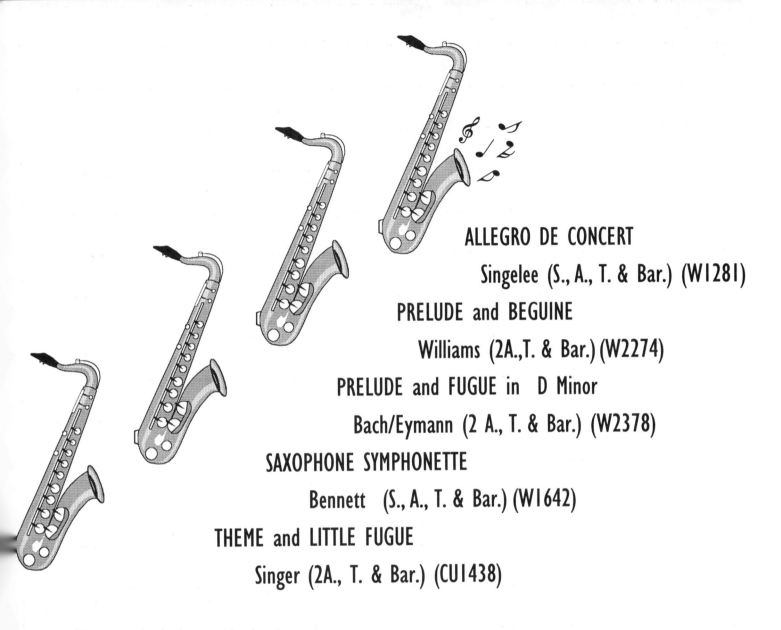

ALLEGRO DE CONCERT
  Singelee (S., A., T. & Bar.) (W1281)
PRELUDE and BEGUINE
  Williams (2A.,T. & Bar.) (W2274)
PRELUDE and FUGUE in D Minor
  Bach/Eymann (2 A., T. & Bar.) (W2378)
SAXOPHONE SYMPHONETTE
  Bennett (S., A., T. & Bar.) (W1642)
THEME and LITTLE FUGUE
  Singer (2A., T. & Bar.) (CU1438)

SAXOPHONE BOOKS

from

CARL FISCHER®

ALL THAT JAZZ Transcribed by S. Isacoff
____ ATJ302 SOLOS for Jazz Tenor Sax
____ ATJ303 SOLOS far Jazz Alto Sax

BASSI
____ 061 27 VIRTUOSO STUDIES (Iasilli)

CAVALLINI 30 CAPRICES (Iasilli)
____ 03776 Volume I
____ 03777 Volume 2

GATTI
____ 01262 STUDIES on Major and Minor Scales (Iasilli)
____ 01263 35 MELODIOUS TECHNICAL EXERCISES

KLOSE
____ 01718 25 DAILY EXERCISES

LABANCHI
33 CONCERT ETUDES (Iasilli)
____ 02329 Book I
____ 02489 Book 2

LESTER
____ 04525 50 RAMBLES for Saxophone

____ 03161 **LET US HAVE MUSIC FOR ALTO SAXOPHONE**

PARES
____ 0784 DAILY EXERCISES & SCALES

RASCHER
____ 05189 DO YOU LISTEN? Exercises for Saxophone Players
(Book and 8 Parts)
____ 02964 TOP-TONES for the Saxophone
(ENGLISH AND GERMAN TEXTS)

SALVIANI
____ 02929 EXERCISES in All the Practical Keys (Iasilli)

SMALL
____ 01835 27 MELODIOUS AND RHYTHMICAL EXERCISES

UNIVERSAL—PRESCOTT
____ 02636 FIRST AND SECOND YEAR
(excerpts from de Ville's Universal Method)

de VILLE
____ 0532 UNIVERSAL METHOD